Module B1 — Understanding Our

Module B1 — Understanding Ourselves

Pages 1-2 — Fitness and Blood Pressure

Q1 systolic, higher, diastolic, lower, mercury
Q2 a) E.g. poor circulation, dizziness and fainting
b) Not enough food and oxygen get to the tissues, particularly the brain.
Q3 a) 23%
b) Possible answers:
The percentage of people with high blood pressure is higher the older the age group. / Over the age of 35, a higher percentage of women than men have high blood pressure.
c) E.g. burst blood vessels, strokes, brain damage, kidney damage, heart disease.
Q4 a) arteries → capillaries → veins
b) The blood pressure will gradually decrease as the blood moves away from the heart.
Q5 Petunia is wrong. Being healthy means being free of any infections and diseases. But being fit is a measure of how well you can perform physical tasks.
Q6 a) A
b) E.g. Any three from: strength, speed, flexibility, agility, cardiovascular efficiency, heart rate, breathing rate.
Q7 Possible answers: He could reduce his weight. / He could try to cut down on the salt in his diet (ready meals and take-aways tend to be high in salt). / He could do more exercise.

Pages 3-4 — Respiration

Q1 a) **glucose** + oxygen → carbon dioxide + **water** + **energy**
b) aerobic
Q2 C
Q3 a) 45 - 15 = 30 breaths per minute
b) During exercise, the rate of aerobic respiration in the muscles increases to provide more energy. The breathing rate increases to provide more oxygen for respiration in the muscles and to remove the extra CO_2.
c) lactic acid
d) Because he has an oxygen debt after the race. Extra oxygen is needed to break down the lactic acid produced by anaerobic respiration in his muscles during the race.
Q4 a) Any two from:
Aerobic respiration releases more energy than anaerobic respiration.
Anaerobic respiration produces lactic acid, which builds up in the muscles, causing them to ache.
Humans can only use anaerobic respiration for short periods.
b) E.g. if they do not have enough oxygen to meet their energy demand by aerobic respiration / if they are exercising vigorously.
c) Josh
d) glucose → lactic acid (+ energy)
Q5 a) Any two sensible answers, e.g.:
Each friend should run for the same length of time at the same speed. / He should measure their pulse rate in the same way.
/ Each friend should be rested with a 'normal' pulse rate at the beginning of the test.
b) Jim

Page 5 — Eating Healthily

Q1

Nutrient	Function
Carbohydrates	Provide energy.
Proteins	Growth and repair of tissues.
Fats	Provide energy and act as an energy store.

Q2 Carbohydrate — Simple sugars
Protein — Amino acids
Fat — Glycerol, Fatty acids
Q3 a) Essential amino acids are amino acids which can't be made by the body.
b) From your diet
Q4 Wendy needs more carbohydrate and protein in her diet because she is more physically active. She needs more protein for muscle development and more carbohydrate for energy.
Q5 a) Food allergies cause more severe reactions than food intolerances and may be fatal.
b) Vegetarians do not eat meat, but do eat animal products (e.g. milk, eggs, cheese). Vegans eat neither meat nor animal products.

Page 6 — Diet Problems

Q1 a) $(5 + 6) \div 100 \times 100 = 11\%$
b) Women, because less than half the obese men interviewed knew that they were obese, whereas over half the obese women interviewed were aware of it.
c) Heart disease, cancers and diabetes should be underlined.
Q2 a) Because foods that contain high levels of protein are often too expensive for, or not available to, the poorest people.
b) $0.75 \times 75 = 56$ g
Q3 a) Possible answers: low self esteem, a poor self-image, anxiety about weight, feeling pressure to look like a celebrity.
b) E.g. Any three from: liver failure, kidney failure, heart attacks, muscle wastage, low blood pressure and mineral deficiencies, tooth decay, mental health problems.
Q4 a) $BMI = 76/(1.7)^2 = 76/2.89 = 26.3$
b) overweight
c) As an athlete, a lot of Daniel's weight could be muscle, so he may not be overweight in the sense of carrying too much fat.

Page 7 — Digestion

Q1 Physical digestion is the breaking down of food by mechanical means (e.g. chewing in the mouth and churning in the stomach and gut). Chemical digestion is the breaking down of food into smaller molecules by chemical means (e.g. enzymes and stomach acid).
Q2 a)

Type of Enzyme	Nutrient broken down	Products of breakdown
Carbohydrase	big carbohydrates, e.g. starch	simple sugars, e.g. glucose
Protease	proteins	amino acids
Lipase	fats	fatty acids and glycerol

b) The small intestine
Q3 Liver, gall bladder, small intestine, neutralises, stomach, enzymes, fats, larger, emulsification.
Q4 The products of carbohydrate and protein digestion **diffuse** directly from the intestines to the blood. The products of fat digestion diffuse out of the gut into the **lymphatic** system. From there, they're emptied into the blood.

Module B1 — Understanding Ourselves

Page 8 — Infectious Disease

Q1 a) Pathogens are micro-organisms that cause disease.
b) Fungi / bacteria / viruses / protozoa.
Q2 a) protozoan, parasite, host, mosquitoes, vector, blood, infected
b) i) Fish could be introduced to the areas where mosquitos lay their eggs to eat the mosquito larvae.
ii) Mosquitos could become resistant to insecticides, but fish will always eat them.
Q3 a) They recognise the antigens on the surface of the pathogen.
b) Yes, because antibodies are always specific so they won't be effective against the new cold pathogen.

Pages 9-10 — Preventing and Treating Infectious Disease

Q1 a) i) True
ii) True
iii) False
iv) False
b) antibodies, another organism, permanent, temporary
Q2 a) Possible answers: It protects you from disease. / If most people in a community are immunised it stops the disease spreading.
b) Possible answers: There may be some short-term side effects, e.g. redness, swelling, mild illness. There is a small possibility of a serious allergic reaction.
Q3 John is protected from infection because his white blood cells can make antibodies to the virus a lot quicker than James's can. When John was immunised, he was given some inactive rubella pathogens. These had antigens on the surface. John's white blood cells then learnt to make the antibodies specific to these antigens.
Q4 Although most of the bacteria causing Sanjay's infection would have been killed, a few bacteria that were most resistant to the antibiotic might survive. These bacteria could reproduce and eventually make a resistant strain.
Q5 The flu is caused by a virus. Antibiotics are only effective against bacterial infections. They won't have any effect on Rachel's illness.
Q6 a)

	1996	2003
Uptake of vaccine	**92%**	**82%**
Number of measles cases	**100**	**440**

b) A decrease in the uptake of the measles vaccine is linked to an increase in the number of cases of measles.
c) When a lot of the population have been vaccinated it is harder for the people who haven't been vaccinated to catch it because there are fewer infected people for them to catch it off.

Page 11 — Other Health Conditions

Q1 Diabetes — Caused by a lack of insulin production
Scurvy — Caused by a vitamin C deficiency
Anaemia — Caused by an iron deficiency
Haemophilia — A genetic disorder
Q2 a) In a benign tumour the cancerous cells do not spread to other sites in the body, but in malignant tumours they can do.
b) Possible answers include: not smoking / wearing sunscreen (and other safe-sun precautions) / a healthy diet / maintaining a healthy body weight / taking regular exercise.

Q3
1. Computer models simulate a response to the drug
2. Drug is tested on human tissue
3. Drug is tested on live animals
4. Human volunteers are used to test the drug

Q4 a) A placebo is a pill that looks like a drug being tested but contains no drug.
b) They use a placebo to make sure it is the actual drug which is causing any effects. Some patients will have beneficial effects just because they *think* they are receiving medicine.
c) A double blind trial is one where neither the scientist doing the test nor the patient knows whether they are getting a drug or a placebo.

Page 12 — Drugs: Use and Harm

Q1 a) A substance which alters the way the body works.
b) Physical addiction means that the body has a physical need for the drug, the person will suffer withdrawal symptoms if no drug is given.
c) The body gets used to the drug and higher doses are needed to produce any / the same effect.
Q2

Type of drug	Example	Effects
Depressants	alcohol / temazepam	Decrease brain activity
Painkillers	aspirin / paracetamol	Reduce the ability of the nerve endings to transmit pain / block nerve impulses
Stimulants	nicotine / ecstasy / caffeine / amphetamines	Increase the activity of the brain
Performance enhancers	anabolic steroids	Help build muscles
Hallucinogens	LSD / cannabis	Distort what is seen and heard by altering the pathways that nerve stimuli usually travel along

Q3 a) Paul, because he supplied the drugs and this is usually given greater punishment than using drugs.
b) Janice, because the drug she used (ketamine) is a class C drug, not class B (like the amphetamines Paul and Duncan took).

Pages 13-14 — Smoking and Alcohol

Q1 a) It can damage brain cells and cause a drop in brain function and memory loss.
b) Drinking alcohol excessively can cause death of liver cells, forming scar tissue that stops blood reaching the liver — this is called cirrhosis.
Q2 a) 2.5 + 2.5 + 1 + 1 = 7 units
b) Douglas drinks 7 units more than the recommended weekly intake.
c) Possible answers: impaired judgement / poor balance / poor coordination / blurred vision / sleepiness.
d) 80 mg of alcohol per 100 ml of blood
Q3 The baby needs oxygen for respiration for growth. If it receives less oxygen from its mother's blood because she is a smoker, it is more likely that the baby will be underweight.
Q4 Carbon monoxide stops haemoglobin carrying as much oxygen.
Nicotine makes smoking addictive. Nicotine is a stimulant drug.
Tar contains carcinogens. Tar covers the cilia in the respiratory tract.
Particulates cause lung irritation.
Q5 a) 70%
b) The number of male smokers aged 35-54 has been decreasing since 1950. The number of female smokers aged 35-54 rose between 1950 and 1970, but then it began to decrease. The number of male smokers aged 35-54 has been consistently greater than the number of female smokers aged 35-54.

CGP

GCSE

Core Science

OCR Gateway

Answer Book

Higher Level

Contents

Published by Coordination Group Publications Ltd.

ISBN: 978 1 84146 715 3

Groovy website: www.cgpbooks.co.uk
Printed by Elanders Hindson Ltd, Newcastle upon Tyne.
Jolly bits of clipart from CorelDRAW®

Based on the classic CGP style created by Richard Parsons

Module B1 — Understanding Ourselves

c) Carcinogens increase the likelihood of mutations in the DNA. If this happens, cell division can go out of control and malignant tumours can form.

Pages 15-16 — Receptors — The Eye

Q1

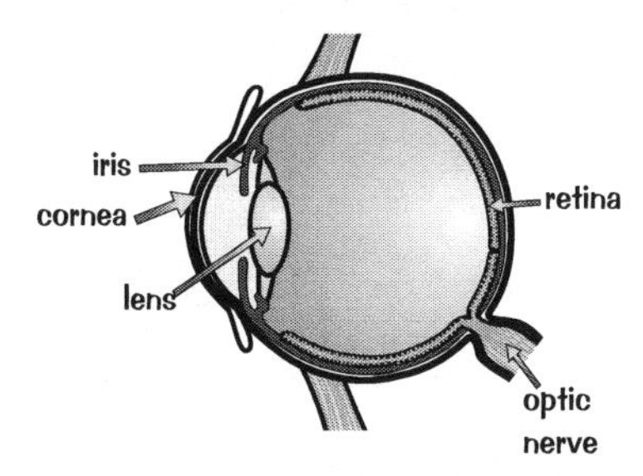

Q2

Part of the eye	Function
Lens	Focuses light on the retina
Optic nerve	Carries impulses from the eye to the brain
Retina	Light sensitive layer
Ciliary muscles	Cause the lens to change shape
Pupil	Hole through which light enters the eye

Q3 Relax, tighten, thin, near, flexibility, convex

Q4 a) i) True
ii) False
iii) True
iv) True
v) False
b) i) inherited
ii) a lack of, cone, retina

Q5 a) i) A: carnivore
ii) Binocular vision enables an animal to judge distances and speeds. This helps the carnivore with catching prey.
b) i) B: herbivore
ii) Monocular vision gives a wider field of vision. This is useful for herbivores in spotting predators.

Page 17 — Neurones and Reflexes

Q1 a) quickly
b) protect
c) without
d) neurones
e) reflex arc

Q2 1 - stimulus, 2 - receptor, 3 - sensory neurone, 4 - relay neurone, 5 - motor neurone, 6 - effector, 7 - response.

Q3 a) It travels as an electrical impulse.
b) This allows the neurone to connect up with many others.
c) It insulates the axon. This speeds up the impulse and stops it getting lost.

Q4 a) It is carried across by a chemical transmitter.
b) Stimulant drugs increase the amount of transmitter chemical at some synapses, which increases the frequency of impulses along the second neurone.

Page 18 — Homeostasis

Q1 Homeostasis is the maintenance of a constant internal environment in the body.

Q2 The following sentence should be ticked: "If your blood glucose level is too high, insulin is secreted and causes glucose to be removed from the blood."

Q3 a) the brain / the thermoregulatory centre
b) The enzymes controlling all the reactions in the human body don't work as well if the temperature varies too much.
c) i) heat stroke
ii) hypothermia

Q4 a) The water in sweat evaporates and transfers heat to the environment, cooling you down.
b) i) Vasodilation is the expansion of blood vessels. Vasoconstriction is the constriction of the blood vessels.
ii) Vasodilation and vasoconstriction allow the body to control the blood flow near the surface of the skin. This allows the body to lose or retain heat in response to the environmental temperature.

Pages 19-20 — Controlling Blood Sugar

Q1 a) from digested food and drink
b) liver and pancreas
c) insulin

Q2 Missing words are: insulin, pancreas, insulin, liver, glucose, blood, reduced / lower.

Q3 E.g.

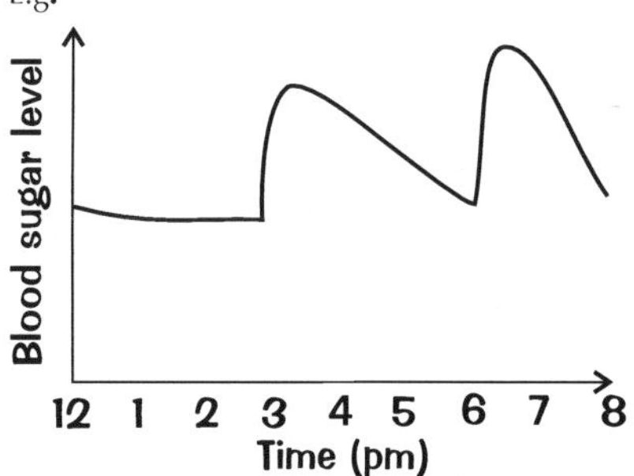

Q4 a) A condition where the pancreas doesn't produce enough insulin.
b) Using a glucose-monitoring device that checks a drop of their blood.

Q5 a) E.g. diet, exercise, by injecting insulin
b) The insulin causes her liver to store glucose from her blood. Eventually her blood sugar levels get so low that she faints (because there isn't enough glucose to release energy for her brain cells to work properly).
c) i) Without insulin none of the sugar in Paul's blood is stored. As Paul digested the food his blood sugar level rose and rose until he eventually lost consciousness.
ii) Paul would be given insulin to bring his blood sugar level down.

Page 21 — Hormones

Q1 a) testosterone
b) oestrogen

Q2 a) Possible answers include: facial hair, increased body hair, deepening of voice, enlargement of the penis and testicles, sperm production, development of muscles.
b) Possible answers include – hips widen, breasts develop, periods start, pubic hair grows.

Q3 a) FSH
b) progesterone
c) oestrogen

Q4 1 - lining of uterus breaks down, 2 - lining of uterus builds up, 3 - egg released, 4 - lining of uterus maintained

Q5 If oestrogen is taken every day, the levels of it are high and this stops the release of eggs (because it inhibits the release of FSH). Because eggs aren't released, the woman taking the pill can't become pregnant.

Module B1 — Understanding Ourselves

Q6 a) FSH
b) Too high a dose of fertility hormones can cause multiple births, such births carry a higher risk for the mother and she might not want / be able to keep them all.

Page 22 — Genes and Chromosomes

Q1 nucleus, chromosomes, DNA, gene
Q2 1) gene, 2) chromosome, 3) nucleus, 4) cell
Q3 a) False
b) True
c) True
d) False
Q4 a) Proteins are made of amino acids.
b) four
c) The order of bases in a gene determines the order of amino acids in the protein — each type of protein has a specific order of amino acids.
d) DNA codes for the proteins made in the cell, and the proteins control the function of a cell.

Pages 23-24 — Genetic Variation

Q1 a) Eye colour: genes
b) Presence or absence of ear lobes: genes
c) Body weight: both
d) Hair length: environment
e) How likely you are to get heart disease: both
Q2

	Can cause variation	Does not cause variation
Formation of gametes from reproductive cells	✓	
Mutation of a reproductive cell	✓	
Random fertilisation	✓	
Conditions in the womb when the baby is developing	✓	
Environmental effects after birth	✓	

Q3 a) i) A gamete is a sex cell, e.g. eggs and sperm.
ii) Gametes are produced from reproductive cells in the ovaries (women) and testes (men).
iii) When reproductive cells split into two to form gametes, some of your dad's genes are grouped with some from your mum. This shuffling up of genes in the gametes leads to variation in the new generation.
b) Fertilisation is the fusion of two gametes (an egg cell and a sperm cell) to create a new cell.
c) The gametes have 23 chromosomes so that when two gametes join together during fertilisation the resulting fertilised cell will have the full number of chromosomes.
Q4 a) A change in the sequence of the DNA bases / a change in the genetic material of an organism.
b) Possible answers include: nuclear radiation, X-rays, ultraviolet light, mutagenic chemicals.
c) Carcinogens
d) They can stop proteins being produced or lead to the wrong proteins being produced or the proteins being malformed.
e) E.g. A mutation in a reproductive cell or an early stage embryo may cause the embryo to die. / The mutated cells might become cancerous. / A mutation could cause a genetic disorder.
f) A mutation may make the organism more suited to its environment and so make it more likely to survive.
Q5 X-rays cause mutations. These mutations will have no significant effect on the adult as it is already fully developed. If the x-rays cause mutations in the sex cells then the offspring will be affected. This is because their characteristics will be determined by one single mutated cell which is copied over and over again as the offspring develop.

Pages 25-26 — Genetic Diagrams

Q1 a) An allele is a variation of a gene.
b) No
c) In a genetic diagram, the allele for a dominant characteristic is a capital letter (e.g. R) and the allele for a recessive characteristic is a lower case letter (e.g. r).
d) homozygous
Q2 a) i) red eyes
ii) white eyes
iii) red eyes
iv) white eyes
b) i)

parent's alleles	R	r
R	RR	Rr
r	Rr	rr

ii) 25% (0.25, 1 in 4, ¼)
iii) There are most likely to be 72 with red eyes (three quarters).
Q3 a)

Parents: Gg, gg
Gametes: G, g, g, g
Offspring: Gg, gg, Gg, gg

b) 1 : 1 (half grey, half white)
c) 6 grey mice, 6 white mice.
Q4 Sally can cross the plants. If the red-flowered plant is RR then all their offspring will be red. If the red-flowered plant is Rr then there will be an approximate 3 : 1 ratio of red to white offspring.
Q5 a) SS
b) ss

Pages 27-28 — Genetic Diagrams and Disorders

Q1 a) True
b) False
c) True
d) False
Q2 a)

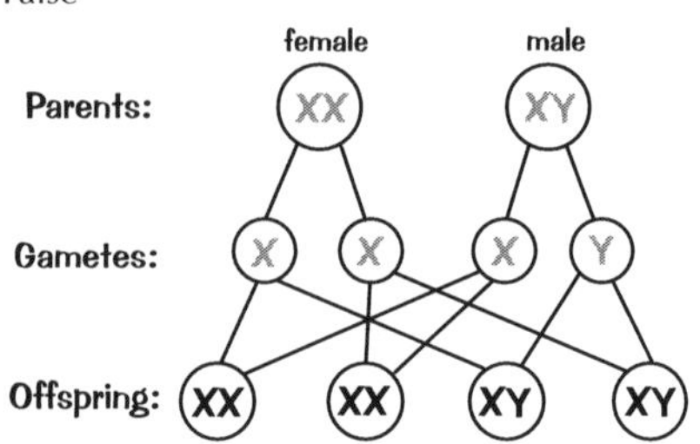

b) 50% (1 in 2, 0.5, ½)
c) Sarah's wrong. It is most likely that half (four) of the children will be boys, but this is only a probability — in reality it might be more or less because there is a 50% chance of having a boy with each pregnancy.
Q3 a) genetic, parents, recessive, allele, pancreas, carrier

Module C1 — Carbon Chemistry

b)

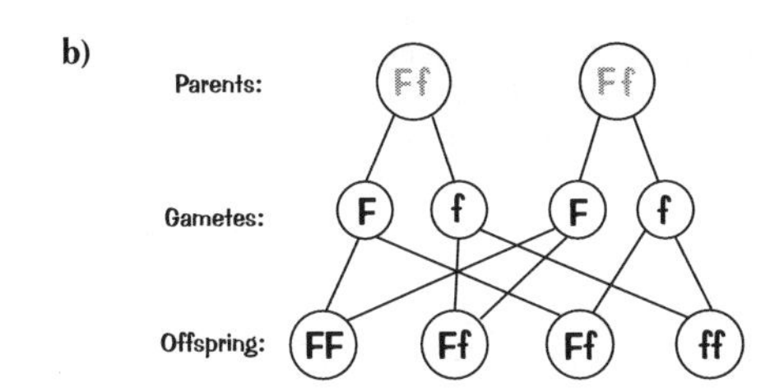

c) i) 25% (1 in 4, 0.25, ¼)
ii) 50% (1 in 2, 0.5, ½)

Q4 a) Possible answers: It might be very traumatic for the parents to have the baby knowing it is likely to die very young. / Pregnancy and childbirth are risky for the mother's health and the risk may not be worth taking if the baby is likely to die. / If the baby does have the genetic disorder and is very ill, it may have a very poor quality of life.

b) Possible answers: It is wrong to take a life. / There is a chance that the baby might be healthy. / An ill baby should have as much right to life as a healthy baby — it isn't moral to terminate the pregnancy because the child is likely to be ill.

Pages 29-31 — Mixed Questions — Module B1

Q1 a) protease
b) Protein is needed for growth and repair of tissue and to regulate cellular processes.
c) i) kwashiorkor
ii) Children need a greater proportion of protein in their diet than adults because they are still growing.

Q2 a) A drug that kills bacteria and fungi without killing your own body cells.
b) The bacteria have been killed by the antibiotic.
c) i) Antibiotic 3.
ii) No, because antibiotics only kill bacteria and fungi. The flu and colds are caused by viruses.

Q3 a) You would expect the pupil to become smaller.
b) Circular muscles contract, to make the iris close up, causing the pupil to become smaller. This is so that less light gets into the eye to prevent damage and aid vision.
c) a reflex action

Q4 a) Glucose is needed for respiration to provide energy for cellular processes.
b) pancreas
c) insulin
d) Homeostasis is the maintenance of a constant internal environment in the body.

Q5 Recessive, because the parents carry the allele, but do not show albinism themselves.

Q6 a) In humans, the males are XY and the females are XX.
b)

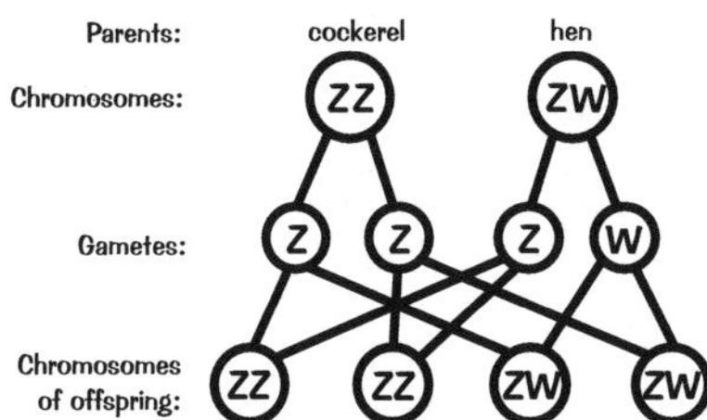

c) 50% (1 in 2, 0.5, ½)

Q7 a) The explosion released nuclear radiation and radioactive material which caused mutations leading to cancer.
b) Cigarette smoke contains mutagens (chemicals which cause cancer).

Module C1 — Carbon Chemistry

Page 32 — Atoms, Molecules and Compounds

Q1 a) electrons
b) nucleus
c) nucleus
d) electrons

Q2 a) two, shared, covalent
b) i) 4
ii) 10

Q3 a) O_2
b) CO_2
c) CH_4
d) H_2O
e) CO
f) C_2H_4

Q4 a) methane
b) CH_4
c) 4
d) C_2H_6
e) 7
f) C_3H_8
g) 10

Q5 a) C_2H_5OH (accept C_2H_6O)
b) 9

Page 33 — Chemical Equations

Q1 $2C + O_2 \rightarrow 2CO$

Q2 a) Reactants: methane and oxygen
Products: carbon dioxide and water
b) methane + oxygen → carbon dioxide + water
c) $CH_4 + 2O_2 \rightarrow CO_2 + 2H_2O$

Q3 a) $CuO + \mathbf{2}\,HBr \rightarrow CuBr_2 + H_2O$
b) $H_2 + Br_2 \rightarrow \mathbf{2}\,HBr$
c) $\mathbf{2}\,Mg + O_2 \rightarrow 2MgO$
d) $2NaOH + H_2SO_4 \rightarrow Na_2SO_4 + \mathbf{2}\,H_2O$

Q4 a) $\mathbf{3}\,NaOH + AlBr_3 \rightarrow \mathbf{3}\,NaBr + Al(OH)_3$
b) $\mathbf{2}\,FeCl_2 + Cl_2 \rightarrow \mathbf{2}\,FeCl_3$
c) $\mathbf{4}\,Fe + \mathbf{3}\,O_2 \rightarrow \mathbf{2}\,Fe_2O_3$
d) $\mathbf{4}\,NH_3 + \mathbf{5}\,O_2 \rightarrow \mathbf{4}\,NO + \mathbf{6}\,H_2O$
e) $MgO + \mathbf{2}\,HNO_3 \rightarrow Mg(NO_3)_2 + H_2O$
f) $CuSO_4 + \mathbf{2}\,NaOH \rightarrow Cu(OH)_2 + Na_2SO_4$

Pages 34-35 — Food Additives

Q1 colouring — makes foods look more appealing
flavour enhancer — improves the natural taste and smell of food
antioxidant — makes food stay fresh for longer
emulsifier — prevents oils separating and floating on top of water

Q2 a) Additives with E numbers have passed a safety test and can be used in the European Union.
b) i) B
ii) A
iii) C
iv) A

Q3 a) oxygen
b) E.g. 2 from: margarine, mayonnaise, jam, sausages, meat pies, other bakery products, instant soup.

Q4 a) i) A
ii) C
b) i) A is the antioxidant because it has prevented the mixture from going off.
ii) C is the emulsifier because it has prevented the oil and water from separating out.

Module C1 — Carbon Chemistry

c) As a control. This provides something to compare other results to and allows you to see what would have happened without an additive.
d) E.g. salad cream, chocolate, ice cream, mayonnaise, margarine and salad dressings such as vinegarettes.

Q5 a)
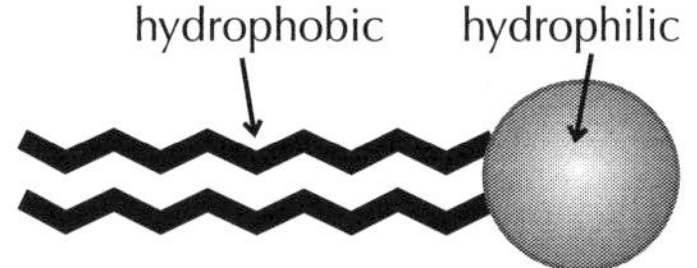

b) Lecithin molecules surround the droplets of oil, with their hydrophilic heads facing out into the water and their hydrophobic tails in the oil droplet. This layer keeps the oil droplets from joining together.

Pages 36-37 — Food Packaging

Q1 a) active
b) intelligent
c) active
Q2 a) Moulds or bacteria grow on food and begin to break it down. This produces unpleasant or poisonous waste products.
b) Most bacteria and moulds can't grow without water.
c) A sachet of a desiccant such as silica gel can be added to the packet to absorb water.
Q3 a) The coloured dot contains a dye which changes colour faster the warmer it gets. It shows if a food's been warm enough for microbes to grow.
b) yes
c) E.g. any two of: How quickly the chicken will go off will depend on what temperature the chicken is keep at / how fresh it was when packaged / how fresh it was when brought.
Q4 a) True
b) False
c) True
d) False
Q5 a) She is investigating how water affects the amount of mould that grows on bread.
b) E.g. any one of: the mass of bread, the temperature, the length of time the bread is left for, the size of the jar, the person estimating the amount of mould.
c) To prevent water getting in or out of the jars.
d) Mould grows faster in moist conditions.
Q6 a) When the button's pressed water and calcium oxide mix and react in an exothermic reaction releasing heat.
b) When the can's opened, water in the gel (in the can) evaporates into a vacuum at the bottom of the can, which cools the drink.

Page 38 — Cooking and Chemical Change

Q1 potatoes — to make them easier to digest
meat — to kill microbes that cause disease
red kidney beans — they are poisonous when raw
Q2 carbohydrate, cellulose, digest, heat
Q3 a) thermal decomposition
b) i) carbon dioxide
ii) You could bubble the gas through limewater — carbon dioxide turns it cloudy.
c) sodium hydrogencarbonate → sodium carbonate + carbon dioxide + water
d) $2NaHCO_3 \rightarrow Na_2CO_3 + CO_2 + H_2O$
Q4 a) The heat energy from cooking breaks some of the chemical bonds in the protein molecule. The protein molecules then change shape.
b) Denaturing the proteins changes the texture of the food and makes it more appealing — less slimy (eggs) or chewy (meat).

Page 39 — Perfumes

Q1 a) E.g. helps to make sure that a chemical isn't poisonous / won't burn or irritate the skin before it is used on humans.
b) E.g. testing may cause pain and suffering to the animals / the animals have no choice about the testing, so it would be fairer to use a human volunteer / chemicals may not affect humans in the same way as they affect the test animal, making the testing useless.
Q2 a) acid + alcohol → ester + water
b) 1. Put 15 cm^3 of ethanoic acid into a 100 cm^3 conical flask.
2. Add 15 cm^3 of ethanol and a few drops of concentrated sulfuric acid.
3. Warm the flask gently on an electric heating plate for 10 minutes.
4. Turn off the heat.
5. When the flask is cool enough to handle, pour its contents into a 250 cm^3 beaker containing 100 cm^3 of sodium carbonate solution.
c) The mixture is heated. / Concentrated sulfuric acid is added.
d) To neutralise the solution.
Q3 a) Compound C, because it won't react with sweat or wash off easily, and it evaporates easily so you'll be able to smell it.
b) E.g. test to check the aftershave is non-toxic / does not irritate skin.

Pages 40-41 — Kinetic Theory & Forces Between Particles

Q1 a) gas
b) solid
c) liquid
d) solid
e) gas
f) gas
g) liquid
Q2 moving, attraction, speeds, quickly, evaporation
Q3 a) It increases because the solid particles gain more energy and vibrate more. This causes them to move apart slightly, increasing the volume that they take up.
b) It increases because the gas particles have gained more energy and are moving faster. This exerts a greater pressure when they bounce off the walls of the container.
Q4 As the temperature increases, more liquid particles gain enough energy to overcome the forces of attraction and become gas particles. These can then move about the room and be detected by the nose.
Q5 a) $X = (45 + 32 + 36) \div 3 = 37.7$
$Y = (112 + 98 + 103) \div 3 = 104.3$
$Z = (278 + 246 + 243) \div 3 = 255.7$
b) The liquid must first evaporate and the vapour must diffuse across the room before it can be detected by the volunteers' noses.
c) B — Liquid X is the most volatile chemical.
d) E.g. a test to see if the compound is toxic, a test to see if the compound has a pleasant smell.

Module C1 — Carbon Chemistry

Page 42 — Solutions

Q1 a) False
b) True
c) True
d) True
Q2 a) salt, iodine, gold
b) water, alcohol, mercury
c) brine, tincture, amalgam
Q3 B and D should be circled.
Q4 a) 10 – 6.8 = **3.2 g**
b) Sodium chloride is more soluble in water than in methanol.
Q5 E.g. any two of: whether the solvent is toxic / whether the solvent is an irritant / how soluble the ink is in the solvent.

Page 43 — Polymers

Q1 The monomer of polyethene is ethene.
Q2 a) A compound that contains at least one double covalent bond between its carbon atoms.
b) High pressure and a catalyst.
Q3 a)

```
   / CH3 H \         / CH3 H \
   |  |  | |         |  |  | |
 n |  C=C  |  -->   -|- C-C -|-
   |  |  | |         |  |  | |
   \  H  H /         \  H  H / n
```

b) polypropene
Q4 a) Ruler 2
b) The forces between the molecules are weaker in ruler 1, which allows the long chains of atoms to slide over one another and to separate more easily.

Page 44 — Polymers and Their Uses

Q1 waterproof, lightweight
Q2

POLYMER	PROPERTIES	USE
polypropene	heat-resistant	kettles
polystyrene foam	thermal insulator	disposable cups
low density polyethene	lightweight	carrier bags
PVC	strong, durable, rigid	window frames

Q3 a) Plastics don't decay, so the landfill sites soon fill up. This is a waste of land and a waste of plastic.
b) Some plastics give off poisonous gases like hydrogen chloride and hydrogen cyanide when they are burned.
c) The different types of plastic all have to be separated out before they can be recycled, which is difficult and expensive.
Q4 a) The coating of polyurethane makes the jacket waterproof.
b) The GORE-TEX® jacket, because it is waterproof but it also allows water vapour from sweat to escape, which is more comfortable during exercise.
c) The PTFE film has tiny holes which let water vapour (from sweat) out, but which are too small for big droplets of liquid water (like rain) to get through. It also repels liquid water. The nylon layer is needed to make the PTFE sturdier.

Page 45 — Alkanes and Alkenes

Q1 a) False
b) True
c) True
d) False
e) False
Q2 a) i) False
ii) True
iii) True
iv) False
b) i) Four
ii) One
Q3 a) C_5H_{12}
b) C_6H_{14}
c) C_8H_{18}
d) $C_{12}H_{26}$
Q4 a) C_2H_4
b)

```
H       H
 \     /
  C = C
 /     \
H       H
```

c) Propene
d)

```
H      H   H
 \     |   |
  C =  C - C - H
 /         |
H          H
```

e) C_4H_8
Q5 Add some bromine water to each substance in two separate test tubes. The bromine water in the test tube containing hexane will stay brown and the bromine water in the test tube containing hexene will decolourise.

Pages 46-47 — Fractional Distillation of Crude Oil

Q1 a) B
b) C
Q2 a) mixture
b) hydrocarbons
c) last
d) larger
Q3

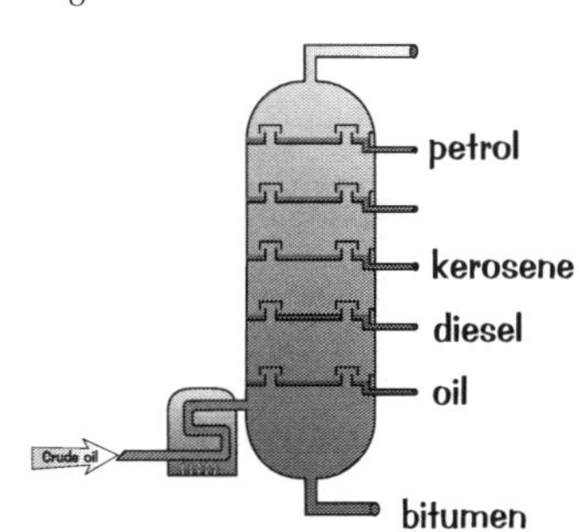

Q4 a) (highest) diesel, kerosene, naphtha, petrol (lowest)
b) (most) diesel, kerosene, naphtha, petrol (least)
c) The more carbon atoms a molecule has, the higher its boiling point is.
Q5 A — heated
B — gases
C — cooler
D — bottom, high
E — smaller
F — fractions

Page 48 — Hydrocarbon Properties — Bonds

Q1 Any three of:
Pentane has a lower boiling point than decane.
Pentane is more flammable than decane.
Decane is more viscous than pentane.
Pentane is more volatile than decane.
Q2 a) pentane, hexane and decane

Module C1 — Carbon Chemistry

b) pentane
c) octadecane
d) pentane

Q3 a)

No. of C atoms	Initial vol. (cm^3)	Vol. after 5 hours (cm^3)	Vol. lost (cm^3)
6	50	8	50 – 8 = 42
10	50	37	50 – 37 = 13
12	50	48	50 – 48 = 2

b) E.g. The temperature that the hydrocarbons are left at. / The size and shape of the evaporating basins that they are left in.
c) The longer the hydrocarbons / the more carbons there are in a hydrocarbon, the less volatile it is.

Q4 Molecules in a liquid have to overcome intermolecular forces to become a gas. Smaller alkanes have weaker intermolecular forces between them, so they turn into gases more easily, and so have lower boiling points.

Pages 49-50 — Cracking

Q1 shorter, petrol, longer, diesel, high, catalyst, molecules, cracking

Q2 a) C — Thermal decomposition
b) B — Energy is needed to break strong covalent bonds.

Q3 a) shorter alkanes and alkenes
b) i) ethene
ii) making plastics
c) 400 °C – 700 °C / high temperatures and the presence of a catalyst e.g. aluminium oxide

Q4 a) kerosene → octane + ethene
b) $C_{10}H_{22} \rightarrow C_8H_{18} + C_2H_4$

Q5 a) kerosene and bitumen
b) petrol
c) Cracking allows the surplus hydrocarbons (mainly larger molecules) to be broken up into smaller molecules for which there is greater demand.
d) E.g. Cracking also produces alkenes that can be sold to companies for making into plastics.

Page 51 — Fuels from Crude Oil

Q1 a) When oil is transported by ship there is the possibility that the ship will crash, spilling oil into the ocean causing big oil slicks. Oil is harmful to birds and sea creatures.
b) Burning oil products produces pollutants such as greenhouse gases, which are linked with global warming, climate change, acid rain and smog.

Q2 energy, non-renewable, increase, more expensive

Q3 a) E.g. any one from: LPG, petrol, kerosene, diesel.
b) E.g. Crude oil is a non-renewable resource. / As crude oil is used up it will become more and more expensive. / Burning fuels from crude oil produces greenhouse gases which leads to global warming. / We currently don't have an alternative to crude oil once it is all used up. / Landfill sites are getting full up.

Q4 a)

Fuel	Initial Mass (g)	Final Mass (g)	Mass of Fuel Burnt (g)
A	98	92	6
B	102	89	13

b) fuel A
c) E.g. any four of: availability, ease of storage, cost, toxicity, ease of use, amount of pollution caused

Page 52 — Burning Fuels

Q1 A — It produces a smoky flame.
C — It produces carbon dioxide.
D — It produces carbon monoxide.

Q2 a) A substance that reacts with oxygen to release useful energy.
b) hydrocarbon + oxygen → carbon dioxide + water
c) i) $CH_4 + 2O_2 \rightarrow CO_2 + 2H_2O$
ii) $C_3H_8 + 5O_2 \rightarrow 3CO_2 + 4H_2O$

Q3 a) Faulty gas fires and boilers may release carbon monoxide into the room which is poisonous.
b) i) complete combustion
ii) a blue flame because it involves complete combustion rather than incomplete combustion.
c) E.g. C_4H_{10} + $\mathbf{4O_2}$ → $\mathbf{5}$ H_2O + CO_2 + **CO** + **2C**

Q4 The water pump draws the gases produced through the tube. The water vapour cools and turns back into liquid in the section with the ice, and you can show it's water by checking its boiling point. The limewater turns milky, showing that CO_2 is also produced.

Page 53 — Energy Transfer in Reactions

Q1 energy, exothermic, heat, an increase, endothermic, heat, a decrease

Q2 a) 29.5 °C – 22 °C = **7.5 °C** (accept 7 °C or 8 °C)
b) neutralisation, exothermic
c) Some energy is always lost to the surroundings.

Q3 a) photosynthesis
b) neutralisation
c) endothermic
d) exothermic

Q4 a) exothermic
b) A–C, because more energy is released when this bond forms than is taken in when the A–B bond is broken.

Page 54 — Measuring the Energy Content of Fuels

Q1 a) energy transferred = mass of water × specific heat capacity of water (4.2) × temperature change
b) energy given out per gram = energy transferred ÷ mass of fuel burned(g)

Q2 a)

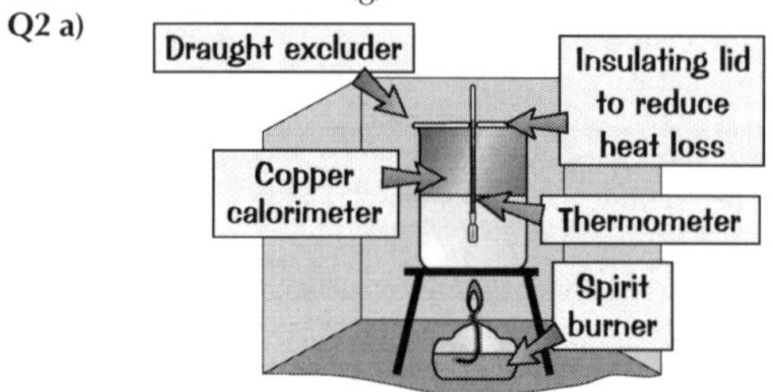

b) E.g. any two of: volume of each fuel; same apparatus — use of lid, material of can, use of draught excluder; mass of water used; distance of spirit burner from can.
c) i) Energy gain = 50 × 4.2 × 30.5 = 6405 J
ii) Energy per gram = 6405 ÷ 0.7 = 9150 J/g = 9.15 kJ/g
d) Energy gain = 50 × 4.2 × 27 = 5670 J
Energy produced per gram = 5670 ÷ 0.8 = 7087.5 J/g = 7.09 kJ/g
e) Petrol would make the better fuel because it releases more energy per gram than fuel X does.

Module P1 — Energy for the Home

Pages 55-57 — Mixed Questions — Module C1

Q1 a) i) The antioxidant slows the reaction of the fat in the ham with oxygen in the air to give products that smell and taste bad.

ii) The silica is a desiccant that absorbs water to keep the air inside the package dry. This makes it difficult for bacteria and mould to grow, as they need water to survive.

b) E.g. people's shopping habits have changed, and they now tend to do one big weekly shop rather than buying what they need daily as they did 50 years ago. / It is easier to transport long-lasting products around the country, which is done a lot more today than it was 50 years ago due to better transport links.

Q2 a) sodium hydrogencarbonate

b) When sodium hydrogencarbonate is heated it undergoes thermal decomposition and releases carbon dioxide. The release of this gas helps the cake rise.

c) The cake mix is a liquid. Although there is some force of attraction between the particles, they're free to move past each other so the substance flows. The cooked cake is solid and has a definite shape because the particles are held in fixed positions.

d) irreversible

Q3 a) It is unsaturated / has a double bond.

b) $n\left(\begin{matrix} H & & H \\ | & & | \\ C & = & C \\ | & & | \\ H & & Cl \end{matrix}\right) \rightarrow \left(\begin{matrix} H & & H \\ | & & | \\ -C & - & C- \\ | & & | \\ H & & Cl \end{matrix}\right)_n$

c) E.g. any one of: window frames, piping, synthetic leather (clothing, accessories, etc.).

d) It's not broken down by micro-organisms so it doesn't rot.

Q4 a) The nail varnish molecules are more strongly attracted to one another than they are to the water molecules.

b) The acetone and nail varnish molecules are more attracted to each other than they are to other molecules of their own type.

c) i) It evaporates easily.

ii) Some of the acetone particles absorb enough energy (e.g. from the warmth of the nail) to overcome the forces of attraction keeping them with the other particles. These then escape as gas particles.

iii) E.g. perfumes. These need to be volatile liquids so that they'll turn into gases easily. They need to become gases so that the particles can move through the air to your nose so you smell them.

Q5 a) Energy transferred = 100 × 4.2 × 22 = 9240 J
Energy per gram = 9240 ÷ 30 = **308 J/g**

b) exothermic

c) The energy released in forming the new bonds.

d) E.g. any one of: availability, ease of storage, cost, toxicity, ease of use, pollution caused.

e) i) carbon dioxide and water

ii) carbon dioxide, water, carbon monoxide and carbon

Q6 a) i)

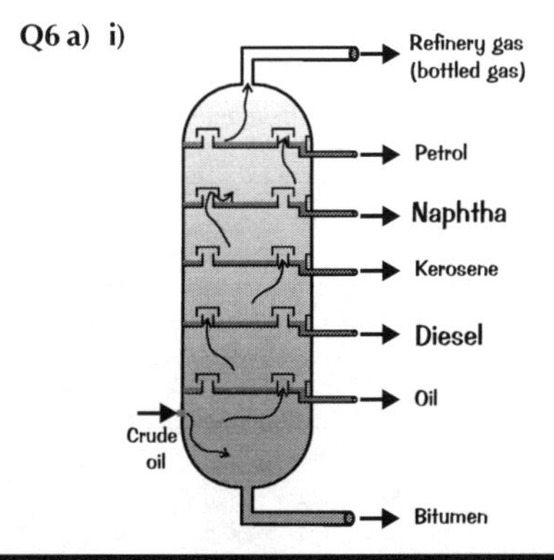

ii) diesel

iii) It contains larger molecules. There are stronger intermolecular forces between larger molecules, which makes it harder for them to escape as gases.

b) The crude oil mixture is heated until most of it has turned into gas. The gases move up the column, gradually cooling as they do so. Different sized molecules turn back into liquids and drain off at different points.

c) Plastics are mostly manufactured from crude oil. This is a non-renewable resource and will one day run out. As it gets used up, the price will rise, so plastics will become increasingly expensive.

Q7 a) Cracking is important because it converts large hydrocarbon molecules, which there is little demand for, into much more useful molecules. It would be difficult to provide enough fuel for transport, heating, manufacture etc. without cracking.

b) A temperature of 400 – 700 °C and an aluminium oxide catalyst.

c) i) $C_{12}H_{26} \rightarrow C_8H_{18} + 2C_2H_4$

ii) hydrocarbon, unsaturated, alkene

iii) Single covalent bonds contain one pair of shared electrons. Double covalent bonds contain two pairs of shared electrons (and are more reactive).

Module P1 — Energy for the Home

Page 58 — Moving and Storing Heat

Q1 Heat is a measure of **energy**
Temperature is a measure of **hotness**.
Heat travels from a **hot** place to a **cold** place.
Water is a good material for storing heat because it has a **high** specific heat capacity.
When a substance is heated its particles vibrate **more** quickly.

Q2 a) Any one of Celsius, Fahrenheit, Kelvin.

b) Heat is measured on an absolute scale. Zero heat means zero movement of particles, and you can't have less than zero movement.

Q3 a) Specific heat capacity is the amount of energy needed to raise the temperature of 1 kg of a substance by 1 °C.

b) Substance A

Q4 Energy = Mass × SHC × temperature change.
The temperature change for both is 50 °C.
Energy from mercury = 27.2 × 139 × 50 = 189 040 J.
Energy from water = 2 × 4200 × 50 = 420 000 J.
Difference = 420 000 – 189 040 = **230 960 J**
(≈ 231 kJ).

Q5 Rearrange the energy equation:
Mass = Energy ÷ (SHC × temperature change).
Mass = 3040 ÷ (380 × 40) = 3040 ÷ 15 200
= **0.2 kg** of copper (or **200 g**).

Pages 59-60 — Melting and Boiling

Q1 Boiling — D
Gas — E
Liquid — C
Melting — B
Solid — A

Q2 C

Q3 a) 60 °C

b) Bonds are forming between particles, which releases energy. This stops the wax from cooling.

c) 10 minutes

Module P1 — Energy for the Home

Q4 To evaporate this mass of water would need 1.5 × 2 260 000 J of energy = 3 390 000 J. The kettle supplies 2 500 J every second, so would need to be on for 3 390 000 ÷ 2500 s = **1356 s** (**22.6 minutes**).

Q5 a) i) Ice needs 334 kJ of energy to melt 1 kg, so 500 kJ of energy would melt 500 ÷ 334 kg = **1.5 kg of ice.**

ii) Zinc needs 110 kJ of energy to melt 1 kg, so 500 kJ of energy would melt 500 ÷ 110 kg = **4.55 kg of zinc.**

b) 30 g of ice completely melts (the mass and exact temp. of the lemonade don't matter). Energy = mass × specific latent heat = 0.03 × 334 000 = **10 020 J** (≈ 10.0 kJ).

c) The energy is used for breaking intermolecular bonds.

Page 61 — Conduction and Convection in the Home

Q1 a) True
b) False
c) True
d) False

Q2 The metal spoon feels colder because metal is a better conductor, so it conducts heat energy away from his hand more quickly.

Q3 A blanket with holes in traps more air than a blanket without holes. This reduces **conduction** as air is a better insulator than the blanket material.

Q4 The very bottom of a hot water tank stays cold... because water isn't a good heat conductor.
Warm air rises... because it is not so dense.
A small heater can send heat all over a room... because heat flows from warm places to cooler ones.

Q5 The experiment shows that convection works very well in water — the ice melts at the top because convection currents carry warm water upwards. It also shows that water is a poor **conductor** of heat — convection currents do not warm the water below the flame, and the water below the heater stays cold because conduction only occurs very slowly.

Pages 62-63 — Heat Radiation

Q1 a) False
b) True
c) True
d) False
e) True
f) True

Q2 Ms Smith's panel has a larger surface area and so it will absorb more heat radiation. Ms Smith's panel is a darker colour and so it will absorb more heat radiation.

Q3 a) Dark, matt surfaces are **good** absorbers and **good** emitters of heat radiation.

b) The best surfaces for radiating heat are **good** absorbers and **good** emitters.

c) The best materials for making survival blankets are **poor** absorbers and **poor** emitters.

d) The best surfaces for solar hot water panels are **good** absorbers and **good** emitters.

Q4 a) By infrared heat radiation.

b) Darker surfaces absorb infrared radiation better than lighter ones, so the brown bread will heat up and toast faster.

c) The middle of the bread is heated by conduction from the surface of the bread. This is a much slower method of heat transfer.

d) The shiny foil will reflect heat radiation onto the underside of Paul's sausages.

Q5 a) i), ii) and iii)

Surface	Reading	Colour and Texture
A	10	**matt black**
B	4	dull silver
C	4	**shiny white**
D	2	**shiny silver**

b) Julie should not say that all such surfaces will emit the same amount of radiation because there will be some variation between different shiny white surfaces and different dull silver surfaces. (She has also assumed that the results are completely accurate. In fact it's likely that errors have been introduced by rounding and experimental error.)

c) D because it emits (and will absorb) the least radiation and so will be best at keeping the food cool.

Pages 64-65 — Saving Energy

Q1 a) Z
b) X
c) Y

Q2 Cost — How much you have to pay.
Cost-effectiveness — How worthwhile it is to spend the money.
Payback time — How long it takes to save as much as you spent initially.
Effectiveness — How much energy you save.

Q3 a) Cavity wall insulation — reduces heat transfer by convection, because pockets of air are trapped in the foam, and can't move between the two walls.

b) Loft insulation — layers of insulation reduce heat transfer by conduction from the ceiling to the roof space. (Heat transfer by radiation from the loft floor is also reduced, because the loft floor is not so warm.)

c) Hot water tank jacket — an insulating layer around the hot water tank reduces heat transfer by conduction and radiation (similarly to loft insulation).

Q4 a) Through the roof — loft insulation.
Through the walls — cavity wall insulation.
Through the doors — e.g. double glazing of any glass panels, draught-proofing strips around the frames and letter box.

b) E.g. She could install double glazing, fit draught-proofing strips around the windows, and have thick curtains. (Or she could turn her heating down.)

Q5 a) Payback time = 1200 ÷ 20 = 60 years.

b) No, because although the shutters are cheaper, they are less cost-effective — they have a longer payback time.

Page 66 — Efficiency

Q1 a) True
b) True
c) False
d) False

Q2 a) **chemical energy** → heat energy.
b) electrical energy → **light energy**.
c) **electrical energy** → **sound energy**.

Q3

Total Energy Input (J)	Useful Energy Output (J)	Efficiency
2000	1500	**0.75**
4000	2000	0.50
4000	**1000**	0.25
600	200	**0.33**

Q4 a) 100 J
b) 5 J

Module P1 — Energy for the Home

c) 95 J
d) 5%

Q5 The winch, like all other devices, is not 100% efficient — some of the input energy will be 'wasted'. Much of this waste is likely to be heat energy, generated by friction in the motor and between the moving parts of the winch.

Page 67 — Electromagnetic Waves

Q1 a) A and C
b) A and B
c) A and C
Q2 a) False
b) False
c) False
d) True
Q3 a) Diffraction
b) Reflection
c) Refraction
Q4

Radio waves	Micro-waves	Infrared		Ultraviolet	X-rays	Gamma rays
$1m-10^4 m$	$10^{-2} m$ (3cm)	$10^{-5} m$ (0.01mm)	$10^{-7} m$	$10^{-8} m$	$10^{-10} m$	$10^{-12} m$

Q5 The shortest wavelength ultraviolet waves overlap the longest wavelength X-rays. Because the wavelengths and frequencies are very similar, they have very similar energy levels and so can be very nearly as damaging.

Pages 68-69 — Wireless Communication

Q1 ionises, ionosphere, quickly, refraction, bounced, short
Q2 **A** and **B** should be circled. **C** is incorrect as this is refraction, not interference.
Q3 a) B
b) Because the wave met the boundary at right angles.
c) The wavelength gets shorter.
d) The frequency remains the same.
e) The wave slows down.
f) The wave would speed up again, the wavelength would increase and the frequency would stay the same.
Q4 a) Wave A is transmitted at a higher angle of elevation.
b) Waves with a higher angle of elevation will take longer.
c) refraction
Q5 a)

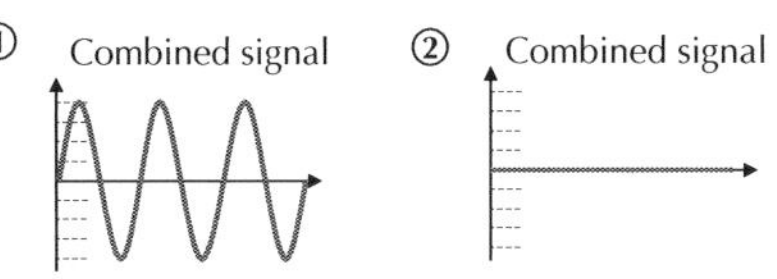

b) For two waves to completely destructively interfere, they must have the same amplitude, the same **wavelength** (or **frequency**) and they must be completely **out of** phase.
c) The two radio signals would interfere with each other because they are on similar frequencies.

Pages 70-71 — Wireless Communication and Ovens

Q1 a) Diffraction
b) The smaller the gap, the more the wave spreads out.
Q2 The false statements are:
b) Microwaves **can't** diffract around large obstacles such as a large block of flats. (Their wavelength is too short.)
c) Microwaves used for communication **aren't** absorbed by the watery atmosphere before they can reach a satellite. (They have a different wavelength to the ones used for cooking.)
Q3 a) Microwaves are absorbed by water in the curry. They make the water molecules vibrate, increasing their heat energy. The heat energy is conducted to other parts of the curry, heating it up.
b) Microwaves only penetrate a couple of centimetres into the curry, so they only heat up the outer bit. It takes time for the heat from the outside to be conducted to the middle. (Stirring would have helped mix the hot and cold bits, which would have reduced the time taken for the temperature to even out.)
Q4 a) Gabrielle's phone doesn't produce a strong enough signal to reach the satellite.
b) i) Carwyn's phone is no longer in the line of sight of a transmitter. The tall buildings have blocked the path of the microwaves, and the microwaves can't diffract around the buildings.
ii) The transmitter needs to be in the line of sight, and putting it on a hill is the easiest way to do that.
Q5 a) You could adjust the size of the gap, and see which detectors picked up a signal. When only the detector nearest the normal line picks up a signal, there's no diffraction. When they all do, there's lots of diffraction, so the gap width must be pretty close to the wavelength — measure it to get the approximate wavelength.
b) The microwaves used in a mobile phone are much weaker than the ones used in a microwave oven. They're also at a different frequency which doesn't heat up water molecules as well.

Page 72 — Communicating with Light

Q1 internal, infrared, reflected, core, dense, pulses, thousands
Q2 a) True
b) False (they are **reflected** along the fibre).
c) True
d) False
Q3

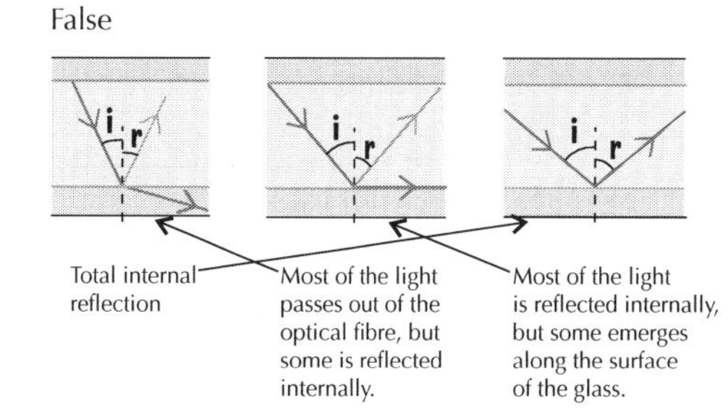

Q4 The angle of incidence above which a ray from the denser medium hitting the boundary will be totally internally reflected.
Q5 E.g. Advantages: Information can be transmitted at a faster rate. It's more secure.
Disadvantages: Cables can be expensive to lay and replace. Information can only be transmitted where there are cables.

Pages 73-74 — Digital Technology

Q1 Digital signals can only have the values 1 or 0. Analogue signals can have any value within their amplitude.

Module P1 — Energy for the Home

Q2 E.g.

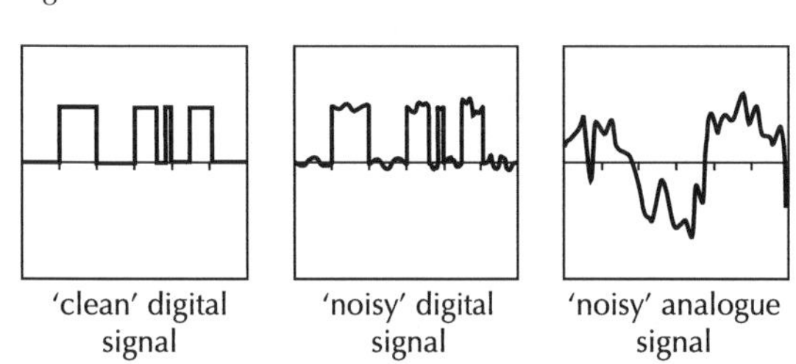

Q3 a) E.g. Analogue 'noise' is amplified when the signal is amplified but digital 'noise' is not. / Low amplitude digital noise can be ignored and so the quality of the signal remains high.
b) Multiplexing means carrying lots of signals on the same electromagnetic wave.
Q4 a) Analogue noise is amplified when the signal is amplified, and digital noise is not. Digital noise doesn't affect whether the signal is 1 or 0.
b) E.g. Digital signals can be multiplexed. Many signals can be carried on the same wire or electromagnetic wave. Signals can also be encrypted.
Q5 a) It's shiny so that the laser light will reflect off it.
b) It is reflected towards the light detector.
c) The beam is reflected from lands and pits slightly differently. The change in the reflected beam can be detected by the light detector and represents the digital 'on's and 'off's.
d) The amplifier makes the signal strong enough so that it can be heard through the loudspeaker
e) i) noise
ii) When an analogue signal is amplified, its noise is also amplified and so the quality of the signal decreases.

Page 75 — Humans and the Environment

Q1 a) Ultraviolet radiation.
b) The DNA in human cells can be damaged or destroyed. / Cells can become cancerous.
Q2 a) The pigment in dark skin absorbs UV, preventing it from reaching the more sensitive cells deeper down.
b) E.g. two from:
Stay in the sun for as short a time as possible.
Wear clothing and hats to reduce the amount of UV absorbed.
Use a protective sun cream.
c) Marie can stay in the sun 25 times as long before burning as she could without any cream on.
Q3 a) The ozone layer is high up in the atmosphere.
b) It absorbs some of the UV rays from the Sun.
c) E.g. CFCs.
Q4 a) False
b) True
c) True
Q5 a) Decrease. When volcanoes erupt they throw a large amount of ash/dust into the air. The ash/dust reflects radiation from the Sun, causing less radiation to get through to Earth.
b) Increase. Carbon dioxide traps heat from the Sun.

Page 76 — Using the Wave Equation

Q1 a) Frequency = half a wave per second = **0.5 Hz**.
b) Speed (velocity) = frequency × wavelength
Speed = 0.5 × 2 = **1 m/s.**
Q2 a) Ten waves every second = 10 Hz
b) speed = frequency × wavelength
= 10 × 0.016
= **0.16 m/s**.
Q3 a) 3×10^8 m/s
b) 9.0×10^7 Hz
c) wavelength = velocity ÷ frequency
wavelength = 300 000 000 ÷ 90 000 000 = **3.33 m**.
Q4 a) wavelength = velocity ÷ frequency
wavelength = 320 ÷ 20 000 = **0.016 m**.
b) frequency = velocity ÷ wavelength
frequency = 320 ÷ 16 = **20 Hz**.
c) sound 320 m/s
light 300 000 000 m/s
so light is approximately 1 000 000 times faster.
Q5 a) 8 minutes is 8 × 60 seconds = 480 seconds. Light travels 150 000 000 000 metres in 480 seconds.
Speed = distance ÷ time = 150 000 000 000 ÷ 480
= **312 500 000 m/s**
(or in standard form, like this: speed = $1.5 \times 10^{11} \div 4.8 \times 10^2 = 0.3125 \times 10^9 = 3.125 \times 10^8$ m/s).
b) 1 mm is 0.001 m, so 1/ 1000 mm is 0.000001 m.
1/2000 mm is half of this = **0.0000005 m (5×10^{-7} m)**.
Frequency = velocity ÷ wavelength
Frequency = $3.125 \times 10^8 \div 5 \times 10^{-7}$ = **6.25×10^{14} Hz**.

Page 77 — Seismic Waves

Q1

Layer	Name	Solid or liquid
A	inner core	Solid
B	mantle	Solid
C	outer core	Liquid
D	crust	Solid

Q2 Disturbances in the Earth produce **seismic** waves which can travel **through** the Earth. These waves can be recorded on a seismograph, which draws a **seismogram**.
Q3 a) P waves are longitudinal.
b) P waves travel faster.
c) S waves cannot travel through the outer core.
Q4 **B** and **C** are true.
Q5 a) They change speed (and hence direction) as the nature of the material of the Earth changes. This is refraction.
b) This happens to P waves e.g. as they enter the outer core, which is a liquid. The change from solid to liquid causes refraction to take place more suddenly.
c) i) S waves don't reach the other side.
ii) This tells us that part of the Earth's interior must be liquid.

Pages 78-80 — Mixed Questions — Module P1

Q1 a) E.g.

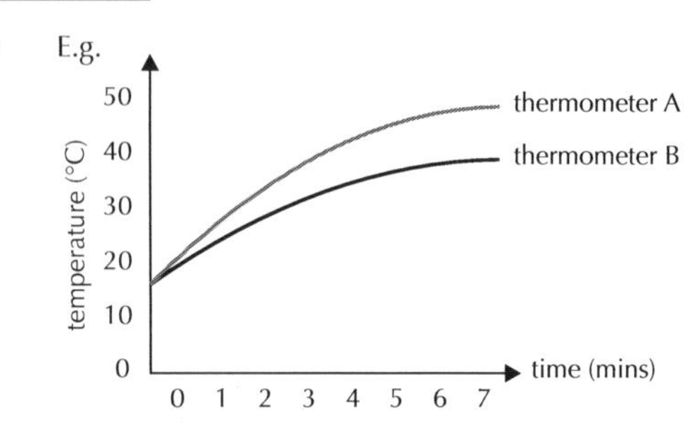

b) The matt black surface is a better absorber of heat radiation (from the Bunsen burner flame) than the shiny silver surface. The matt black surface is also a better emitter of radiation, so the temperature rise for A will be quicker/steeper than for B.

Module B2 — Understanding Our Environment

Q2 a) The freezer compartment cools the warmer air at the top of the fridge, which then falls, forcing warmer air to rise.

b) Efficiency = Useful Output Energy ÷ Total Input Energy. The total input energy must equal the total output energy, i.e. 168 J.
So efficiency = 100 ÷ 168 = **0.60** (or 60%).

Q3 a) Visible light or infrared.

b) E.g.

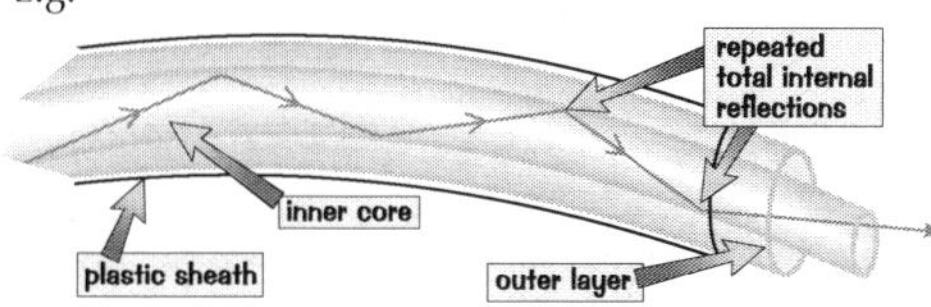

Q4 a) Over 5 years, the savings would be:
Hot water tank jacket: (5 × £20) – £20 = £80
Draught-proofing: (5 × £70) – £80 = £270
Cavity wall insulation: (5 × £85) – £650 = –£225
Thermostatic controls: (5 × £30) – £140 = £10
So **draught-proofing** would save the most money.

b) The temperature change required is 36 – 14 = 22 °C.
Energy = mass × SHC × change in temperature
= 90 × 4200 × 22 = **8 316 000 J** (= 8316 kJ = 8.316 MJ).

c) Mass = Energy ÷ Specific Latent Heat
= 8 316 000 ÷ 334 000 = **24.9 kg** of snow.

Q5 a) i) crust
ii) mantle
iii) outer core
iv) inner core

b) P-waves (because they can pass through the Earth's liquid outer core).

c) The properties of the mantle change *gradually*, causing the wave to change speed and be refracted (change direction) gradually as it progresses. At the boundary with the outer core there is an *abrupt* change in properties, so the wave changes direction abruptly.

Q6 a) A
b) B
c) E.g. Use of products (such as hairsprays and fridge coolants) which release CFCs into the atmosphere has caused a thinning of the ozone layer (which absorbs UV radiation from the Sun). / People spend more time sunbathing.
d) E.g. a volcano / an asteroid impact

Q7 a) Frequency = speed ÷ wavelength
= 3×10^8 m/s ÷ 1500 m = **200 000 Hz** (= 200 kHz).

b) Longer waves diffract more around large objects than shorter waves. So the long-wave radio signal diffracts around the mountains and can be received in Mr Potts' holiday cottage. The short-wave radio and TV signals (which also use short waves) don't diffract much and so they can't be received in his cottage.

c) i) The signals are very close in frequency, so they may interfere with one another and cause very 'noisy' reception.
ii) Broadcast digital signals, which suffer less from interference.

d) They have different wavelengths/frequencies. The microwaves used for cooking are readily absorbed by water molecules (in the food) so that they heat the food. Those used in mobile phone networks are not absorbed much by water molecules, so they pass through clouds.

Module B2 — Understanding Our Environment

Page 81 — Ecosystems

Q1 a) In natural ecosystems humans have no control over the processes, but in artificial ecosystems humans deliberately promote some organisms and eliminate others.
b) Two from:
farms, fish farms, market gardens, greenhouses etc.
c) Artificial ecosystems — there's less biodiversity as pest species are reduced or even lost completely.

Q2 natural, interference, diversity, natural, pollution, rainforests, species

Q3 a) It's the breeding season — lots of small fish were born, so the average size fell when they were included in the calculations.
b) E.g. a high number of fish lice and an increased water pH.
c) In this experiment the fish farm (Ecosystem A) did produce larger fish and more fish survived.

Page 82 — Classification

Q1 a) i) kingdom
ii) genus
iii) species
b) A group of closely-related organisms that can breed to produce fertile offspring.

Q2

	Plant	Animal
Travels to new places		✓
Hunts for food		✓
Fixed to the ground	✓	
Compact body		✓

Q3 a) Vertebrates have an internal skeleton with a backbone. Invertebrates lack an internal skeleton (although they may have an exoskeleton).
b) Frog — Amphibian — Moist, permeable skin, lay eggs in water
Horse — Mammal — Furry skin, produce live young, produce milk
Snake — Reptile — Dry, scaly skin, lay leathery eggs on land
Sparrow — Bird — Feathers, most fly, mouth adapted into beak
Herring — Fish — Scales and fins, live and lay eggs in water

Q4 a) It shows features of more than one vertebrate class. / It shows features of birds and reptiles.
b) Long bony tail, claws and sharp teeth.
c) Laid eggs. Archaeopteryx has features of a reptile and a bird — both of these classes lay eggs.

Page 83 — Species

Q1 a) Binomial means a two-part name (one name for the genus and one for the species).
b) Homo sapiens
c) sapiens

Q2 Tigers and lions are different species so the offspring they produce are hybrids, not genuine species. Hybrids are always infertile.

Q3 a) It is a fern. (It does not produce seeds, but does have long stems with lots of small leaves.)

Module B2 — Understanding Our Environment

b) No, because the plant might have other features e.g. flowers, that can't be seen in the sample / the plant might flower or produce seeds at a different time of year.

Q4 a) E.g. feed on fish, similar habitats, similar body shapes.

b) Sharks have gills and most lay eggs. Dolphins breathe using lungs and give birth to live young.

c) Sharks: fish   Dolphins: mammals

Page 84 — Populations

Q1 a) A quadrat

b) Total area = 250 m x 180 m = 45 000 m^2
Total area x number of plants = population
45 000 m^2 x 11 = **495 000**, so there's likely to be approximately 500 000 clover plants.

c) i) (11 + 9 + 8 + 9 + 7) ÷ 5 = 8.8 plants

ii) (It is the same field, so use 45 000 m^2 again.)
45 000 m^2 x 8.8 = 396 000 clover plants (≈ 400 000).

d) Lisa's result is likely to be more accurate as she has used a larger sample size.

Q2 a) nets, pitfall traps, marked, released

b) Capture another sample of the population in the same way and count how many are marked.

Q3 Population size = (no. animals in first sample × no. animals in second sample) ÷ no. of marked animals in second sample
Population size = (30 × 30) ÷ 7 = 128 ≈ 130.

Pages 85-86 — Photosynthesis

Q1 a) It enables plants to make their own food.

b) carbon dioxide + water → glucose + oxygen

c) chloroplast — the structure in a cell where photosynthesis occurs
chlorophyll — a green pigment needed for photosynthesis
sunlight — supplies the energy for photosynthesis
glucose — the food that is produced in photosynthesis

Q2 a) 00.00 (midnight)

b) There's no light at night, so photosynthesis won't occur.

c) Plants use the food / glucose from photosynthesis that they have stored during the day.

d)

Q3 a) lipids

b) starch

c) nitrates

d) cellulose

Q4 a) leaves / stem (any green part)

b) Glucose is used to make proteins and cell walls. It is also needed for respiration to produce energy for growth.

Q5 a) They change stored starch to glucose and use it for respiration to release energy for growth.

b) They use their leaves to make glucose by photosynthesis.

c) Starch is insoluble, which means the tubers don't become bloated by osmosis. They would swell up too much if they contained glucose.

Q6 leaves, energy, convert, cells, cellulose, walls, lipids, margarine

Q7 $6CO_2 + 6H_2O \rightarrow C_6H_{12}O_6 + 6O_2$

Pages 87-88 — Rate of Photosynthesis

Q1

	Photosynthesis	Respiration
Requires energy	✓	✗
Releases energy	✗	✓
Occurs both day and night	✗	✓
Occurs daytime only	✓	✗
Produces glucose	✓	✗
Releases oxygen	✓	✗
Is dependent on temperature	✓	✓
Will increase the levels of atmospheric carbon dioxide	✗	✓

Q2 a) E.g. light intensity, CO_2 concentration, temperature

b) A factor that stops photosynthesis from happening any faster.

c) E.g. time of day (such as night time) / position of plant (such as in the shade) / amount of sunlight / temperature etc.

Q3

Change in conditions	Environmental factor(s) changed	Effect on photosynthesis
An oil stove is turned on.	carbon dioxide temperature	increase
A cooling fan is switched on.	temperature	decrease
More plants are added to the room.	carbon dioxide	decrease
Jacquie's family enter the room.	carbon dioxide temperature	increase
An electric heater is switched on.	temperature	increase
A light bulb is switched on.	light	increase
The blinds are closed and lights switched off.	light also accept temperature	decrease

Q4 a) Two from: amount of light, temperature, availability of water.

b) The faster the rate of photosynthesis, the faster the growth rate of the grass.

Q5 a)

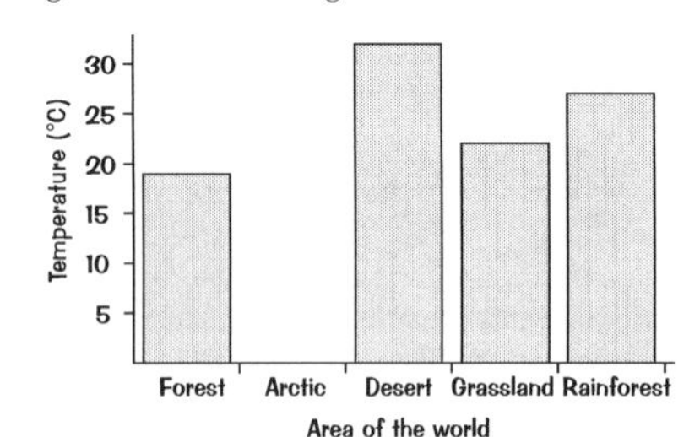

b) Arctic

c) The temperatures are extremely low there, so the rate of photosynthesis will be slower because the enzymes needed for photosynthesis will be working very slowly.

d) Despite the high temperatures, few plants grow in the desert because there is not enough water in the desert for most plants to survive.

Q6 $C_6H_{12}O_6 + 6O_2 \rightarrow 6CO_2 + 6H_2O$

Page 89 — Interactions Between Organisms

Q1

Factor	Plants only	Animals only	Both
The amount of water available.			✓
The total amount of food available.			✓
The amount of light available.			✓
The minerals in the soil.	✓		
The quality and amount of shelter.			✓

Q2 species, habitat, foods, resources, adapted

Q3 a) Predator: heron   Prey: frog

b) The number of frogs will decrease.

c) e.g. increase in number of herons, lack of food

Module B2 — Understanding Our Environment

d) If the number of frogs decreases then the number of herons will fall because there is less food (frogs) for them.

Q4 a) In a parasitic relationship, parasites live off a host but give nothing back. In mutualism, both organisms benefit.

b) e.g. nitrogen-fixing bacteria in the nodules of legumes
OR the 'cleaner' animals, like the oxpecker birds found on the backs of buffalo.

Pages 90-91 — Adaptation

Q1

Feature	Wind pollinated	Insect pollinated
Large, often feathery stigma.	✓	
Brightly coloured petals.		✓
Sticky pollen grains, can be large.		✓
Petals small or absent completely, but stigma exposed.	✓	
Light, dry pollen grains.	✓	
Scented flowers (usually petals and nectar).		✓

Q2 a) the kangaroo rat

b) the polar bear

c) The polar bear has a rounded body shape, which means it has a small surface area for its volume (a sphere has the smallest ratio).

d) Less heat can be lost (for a given volume).

e) bigger

f) It allows the kangaroo rat to lose heat more quickly than the polar bear, which is important in the hot desert.

Q3 water, small, concentrated, sweat, night

Q4 a) In the desert.

b) i) The cactus has spines instead of leaves, because the small surface area gives less of a surface for water to evaporate from. / The spines help to protect the cactus from being eaten by animals.

ii) The cactus has a thick, fleshy stem where it can store water. / The stem can photosynthesise.

iii) The cactus has shallow but very extensive roots, so it can take in as much water as possible when it rains / it has a long tap root to reach water deep underground.

Q5 a) Reading down the table: 3:1, 1.5:1, 1:1, 0.75:1, 0.6:1 (accept just the numbers).

b) The surface area : volume ratio decreases as the size of the cube increases.

c) The smallest cube, because it has a smaller volume where it can hold heat but a larger surface over which it can lose it.

d) A mouse is small so it would lose heat quickly. Fur provides a layer of insulation to reduce heat loss.

Q6 a) The camel's hump is used to store fat which can be used for energy on long journeys where there's no food. Having most of the fat in the hump means the rest of the body isn't insulated, helping heat loss.

b) The thick coat reflects sunlight in the day to keep them cool and keeps them warm at night when it's cold.

Pages 92-93 — Fossils

Q1 a) evolution

b) Bits that don't decay easily — teeth, bones, shells etc.

Q2 a) E.g. Longer legs would help when running away from predators. B has a hoof rather than toes. This makes it more stable when running. The environment may have changed from rocky slopes or swamps (where toes would help with balance) to flat plains (where balance is less important).

b) E.g. the fossils of C perhaps simply didn't happen to form. Only a small proportion of dead organisms form fossils. Alternatively, fossils may have formed and not yet been discovered.

Q3a) The shell will eventually be replaced with minerals as the sediments around it turn to rock.

b) Fossils of animals are more common as animals tend to have harder tissues than plants.

c) Fossil B is in a lower layer of rock. It's likely this layer formed first. Subsequent layers built up on top.

Q4 a) Any two from: from casts and impressions, by gradual replacement by minerals, from preservation in conditions where there is no oxygen.

b) bones, slowly, rock, shaped, clay, hardens, cast

Q5 a) i) Amber is fossilised tree sap or resin.

ii) There's no oxygen or moisture in amber, so decay microbes can't survive to decay dead organisms. Thus, dead organisms are preserved.

b) No oxygen or moisture — Tar pits
Too acidic — Peat bogs
Too cold — Glaciers

Q6 a) Scientists could claim that the skull came from a species whose ancestors were like chimps and which eventually evolved into humans — a 'missing link' to support the theory that humans evolved from chimp-like ancestors.

b) Creationists would say that the skull belonged to a species of organism created individually by God, which is now extinct.

Pages 94-95 — Theories of Evolution

Q1 a) 1. All giraffes had short necks.
2. The giraffes competed for food from low branches. This food started to become scarce. Many giraffes died before they could breed.
3. A giraffe was born with a longer neck than normal. The long-necked giraffe was able to eat more food.
4. The long-necked giraffe survived to have lots of offspring that all had longer necks.
5. More long-necked giraffes survived to breed, so more giraffes were born with long necks.
6. All giraffes have long necks.

b) Giraffes would have stretched their necks straining to reach the leaves. Their longer necks were passed on.

Q2 a) People with sickle cell anaemia may become very ill. They are less likely to survive and reproduce than people without the disease.

b) In Africa malaria kills huge numbers of people. People with the sickle cell allele are more likely to survive to reproduce in areas where large numbers of people are dying of malaria.

Q3 A small number of the original bacteria were naturally resistant to the antibiotic. These bacteria survived the antibiotic and reproduced to form the second colony. All the bacteria in the second colony inherited the antibiotic resistance.

Q4 The following statements should be ticked:
All organisms face a struggle to survive.
If an animal or plant is to survive in a changing environment, it needs to adapt.
Characteristics are passed on through reproduction from parent to offspring.

Q5 a) Rats that are resistant to warfarin are more likely to survive, so this genetic resistance to warfarin has been selected for in the population.

b) Darker tree trunks in polluted industrial areas mean darker moths are better camouflaged, so have been selected for in the population.

Module B2 — Understanding Our Environment

c) Some malaria parasites are resistant to the drugs, so this drug resistance is selected for in the population. After a while the population becomes too resistant for a drug to be effective, so a new drug is required.

Q6 a) some religious people

b) Darwin's theory contradicted the views of religious people, who believed that all species had been created as they are now, by God.

Pages 96-97 — Human Impact on the Environment

Q1 a) bigger

b) faster

c) greater

Q2 a) 1970

b) About 1 million tonnes.

c) Acid rain

Q3 a) The UV rays that enter through the hole kill the plankton that the whales feed on.

b) CFC gases (found in polystyrene, aerosols, air-conditioning units, fridges etc.)

c) UV rays increase the risk of skin cancer.

Q4 a) An indicator species.

b) Collect samples of the same size, in the same way, at the same time of day, etc.

c) Mayfly larvae prefer clean water and sludgeworms prefer water that contains sewage.

d) E.g. Sewage is full of bacteria, which use up a lot of oxygen. Animals like mayfly larvae might not have enough oxygen to survive.

Q5 a) False (highly developed countries tend to cause more pollution per person)

b) True

c) True

d) False (other thing such as cars also pollute)

e) False (lichens prefer clean air)

f) False (some animals thrive in polluted conditions, some have adapted to make that ecological niche their own)

Q6 exponentially, more, environment, resources, pollution, developed, higher, pollution, population

Page 98 — Endangered Species

Q1 a) E.g. Greenpeace and the RSPB provide education programmes, and the National Trust preserves sites and habitats.

b) No

c) An ecosystem created by humans, such as botanical gardens.

d) Captively bred animals can be released to increase wild populations and reintroduced to areas where the species has died out.

Q2 conservation, endangered, restrictions, ensuring, control, ladybirds, aphids, pesticides

Q3

Effect	Human Action	Alternative / remedy
Climate change	Burning fossil fuels	E.g solar, nuclear or wind power
Destroying habitats	Chopping down trees	E.g. replanting programmes
Extinction of animals	Hunting animals	E.g. legal restrictions on hunting
Harmful water pollution	Using pesticides	E.g. use biological pest control
Increased competition between species	Introducing new species	E.g. only introduce new species in secure environments

Page 99 — Sustainable Development

Q1 a) False (it can protect them and their habitats)

b) False

c) True

d) False (whale products have been used to make cosmetics)

e) False (most whaling is controlled internationally)

f) True

g) False (we have learnt a lot from observing behaviour of captive whales)

Q2 a) Any 2 sensible suggestions, such as: polluting the environment, overusing resources, reducing biodiversity.

b) Any sensible explanation, e.g. It can be difficult to clean areas that have been polluted. When species become extinct they are lost forever. Sensitive and ancient habitats like rainforest will not easily grow back.

c) Development that meets the needs of today's population without harming the ability of future generations to meet their own needs.

Q3 a) Fishing quotas have been introduced to prevent over-fishing.

b) Trees are now planted to replace the ones they take out (and more paper is now recycled).

Q4 Education makes people aware of the importance of sustainability and helps them to make sustainable choices, for example about the things they buy.

Pages 100-102 — Mixed Questions — Module B2

Q1 a) E.g.

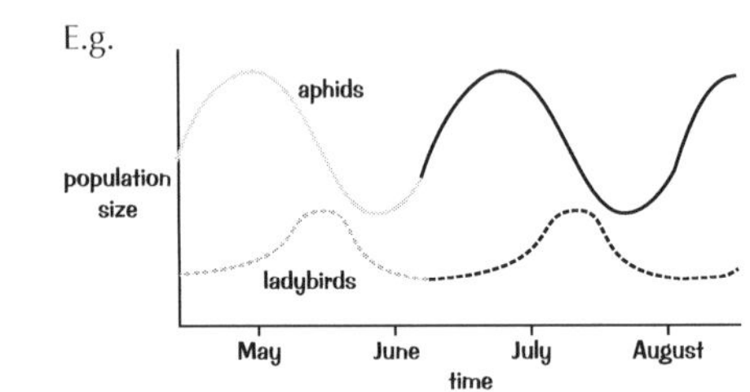

b) Ladybird numbers can only build up if their food (aphids) builds up first. When aphid numbers decrease there isn't enough food to sustain a large population of ladybirds so the number of ladybirds falls shortly afterwards.

c) Catch a sample of the ladybirds and mark them. Release the ladybirds. Catch a second sample of ladybirds in the same way as the first sample and count the number of marked ladybirds. Then calculate the estimate.

Q2 a) Increasing the concentration of carbon dioxide increases the rate of photosynthesis (up to a certain point).

b) The rate of photosynthesis does not continue to increase because temperature or levels of carbon dioxide act as limiting factors.

Q3 a) Because they occupy the same niche — they eat the same food, use the same type of nesting sites etc.

b) E.g. any two from:
Educate people about how they can help the red squirrel.
Protect the red squirrels' habitats.
Legally protect the red squirrel from hunting and habitat damage.
A captive breeding and release programme for the red squirrel.
Create artificial ecosystems for the red squirrels to live in.
Reduce the number of grey squirrels, e.g. through a cull.

Module C2 — Rocks and Metals

Q4 a) Fossil X, because older rocks are generally deeper.
b) Most animals have hard parts in their bodies e.g. bones or shells. These parts are fossilised more easily.
c) If two organisms can reproduce and produce fertile offspring then they are of the same species. It is not possible to tell if two fossilised animals would have been able to do this.
d) If two different species live in similar environments they may evolve similar features so that they are both adapted to their environment.
Q5 a) i) It rises.
ii) It stays the same.
b) the goat
c) They lose water too quickly and it's difficult to find water in the desert.
Q6 a) The second Latin name, which gives the species, is different for the two geese.
b) They belong to the same genus. / The first Latin name is the same.
c) the binomial system
d) E.g. feathers, ability to fly, beak.
Q7 a)

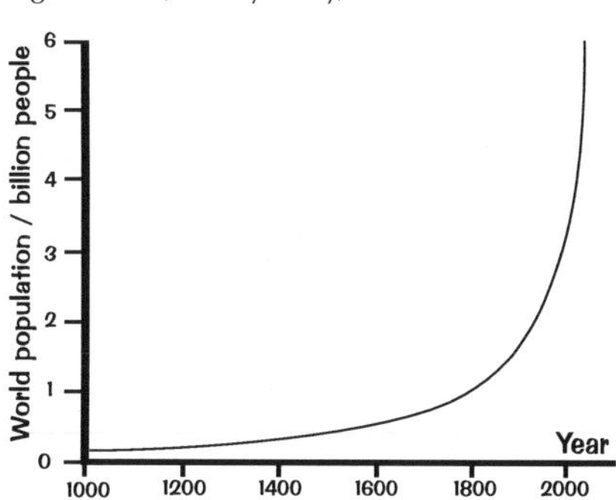

b) E.g. Look for indicator species in the water near to the factory. Bloodworms, water lice, rat-tailed maggots and sludgeworms are all indicators of polluted water.
c) Natural ecosystems because they are largely left unmanaged by people.

Module C2 — Rocks and Metals

Page 103 — Paints and Pigments

Q1 pigment — gives paint its colour
colloid — tiny particles dispersed in another material
solvent — keeps paint runny
binding medium — holds pigment particles to a surface
Q2 a) oil-based, water-based
b) solvent
c) something that dissolves oil
Q3 a) i) oil-based
ii) Some of the solvents may produce harmful fumes, so e.g. make sure there's plenty of ventilation.
b) Water-based – most of the paint sold is used for internal decoration. This is most likely to be water-based.
Q4 a) False
b) False
c) True
d) True
Q5 a) There's no oxygen in space so oil cannot oxidise and harden.
b) There's no gravity in space so paint must be sticky to stay put.

Page 104 — Dyes and Special Pigments

Q1 natural, indigo, purple, synthetic, thermochromic, phosphorescent
Q2 Phosphorescent pigments — used in emergency exit signs, glow in the dark, used in road signs, store light energy
Thermochromic pigments — can become transparent when heated, used in thermometers, used in kettles that change colour when they boil
Q3 a) i) radioactive paint
ii) phosphorescent paint
b) radioactive paint gives off radiation which can be harmful.
Q4 E.g. any 2 from: thermometers, mugs that warn the user that the contents are hot, drink cans that let you know when the contents are cold enough to drink.

Page 105 — Construction Materials

Q1 cement — limestone, clay
bricks — clay
iron — ores
aluminium — ores
concrete — limestone, clay, sand, gravel
Q2 a) melting, calcium carbonate, silicon dioxide, sodium carbonate
b) clay, fired, bricks
c) clay, cement
Q3 a) It's a combination of steel and concrete.
b) It is stronger than normal concrete.
Q4 a) E.g. any 3 from: uses up land, destroys habitats, transporting rock causes noise and air pollution, noise of explosives and dust from quarry itself, waste materials produce unsightly tips.
b) E.g. disused sites can be dangerous. Disused mines can collapse and there may be subsidence. Also, jobs will be lost, people will move away and local services such as healthcare and transport may suffer.

Page 106 — Extracting Pure Copper

Q1 a) E.g. by reducing it with carbon.
b) Purified copper conducts better, so is needed for electrical conductors.
c) impure (boulder) copper
d) The electrons come off the atoms of pure copper at the anode, giving Cu^{2+} ions. These positive ions are attracted to the negative cathode, where the ions gain electrons to make them copper atoms again. These copper atoms bind to the cathode.
Q2 Cathode: $Cu^{2+} + 2e^- \rightarrow Cu$
Anode: $Cu \rightarrow Cu^{2+} + 2e^-$
Q3 The following boxes should be ticked:
It's cheaper than mining new copper.
It uses less energy and therefore less fossil fuel.
Less carbon dioxide is produced as a result.
Q4 The impurities are not charged (i.e. they are neutral) so they are not attracted to the cathode.
Q5 Cathode: $Ag^+ + e^- \rightarrow Ag$
Anode: $Ag \rightarrow Ag^+ + e^-$
Q6 The copper produced will have zinc impurities in it.

Module C2 — Rocks and Metals

Pages 107-108 — Alloys

Q1 alloy, non-metal, carbon, brass

Q2 a) i) True
ii) False
iii) False
iv) True
v) True
vi) False
vii) False

b) Steel — car bodies, cutlery, girders
Bronze — bells, sculptures
Brass — musical instruments, doorknobs
Amalgam — teeth fillings
Nitinol — shape retaining spectacle frames

Q3 a) harder, stronger, more
b) 90%
c) Hi-copper bronze

Q4 a) There would be little time to make the join.
b) The car body could be returned to its original shape after being dented.
c) Brass is harder than copper.
d) Copper and tin would corrode much faster than bronze.
e) i) Steel is stronger than iron.
ii) Steel is less likely to rust than iron.

Page 109 — Building Cars

Q1 rusting, iron, water, iron(III) oxide, oxidation, salty

Q2 **Steel — advantage:** E.g. reasonably strong, easy to bend into shape (malleable), can be welded together, fairly cheap, fairly resistant to rust (compared to iron).
disadvantage: E.g. fairly heavy, will corrode eventually.
Aluminium — advantage: E.g. strong, low density, easy to bend into shape (malleable), very resistant to corrosion.
disadvantage: E.g. expensive, can't be welded together.

Q3 Dashboard — Material: plastic; Advantage: light and hardwearing.
Windows — Material: glass; Advantage: Transparent.
Seats — Material: Natural and synthetic fibres; Advantage: light and hardwearing.
Electrical wiring — Material: Copper; Advantage: Electrical conductor.

Q4 a) True
b) False (by law, in 2015 95% of the car should be recyclable)
c) False (it's difficult to sort out the non-metal bits of the car)
d) True

Pages 110-111 — The Three Different Types of Rock

Q1 igneous rocks — formed when magma cools — granite
metamorphic rocks — formed under intense heat and pressure — marble
sedimentary rocks — formed from layers of sediment — limestone

Q2 Igneous, crust, slowly, big, intrusive, granite, gabbro, quickly, small, extrusive, basalt, rhyolite

Q3 a) E.g. the church is made from limestone which is formed mostly from sea shells.
b) Pressure forces out water. Fluids flowing through the pores deposit minerals that cement the sediment together.
c) They are both the same chemical — calcium carbonate.

Q4 sedimentary, heat, texture, metamorphic, magma, igneous, crystals.

Q5 a)
1. Sea creatures die.
2. Dead sea creatures become buried in sediment.
3. Several layers of sediment build up and compress the lower layers.
4. Natural mineral cement sticks the sediment together and limestone forms.
5. Heat and pressure causes limestone to change into marble.

b) Limestone is made of bits of calcite (mostly crushed seashells) cemented together. Marble is made up of small crystals. This gives it a more even texture than limestone and makes it much harder.

Q6 a) Thermal decomposition is when one substance chemically breaks down into at least two new substances when it's heated.
b) Word equation: calcium carbonate → calcium oxide + carbon dioxide
Symbol equation: $CaCO_3(s) \rightarrow CaO(s) + CO_2(g)$

Pages 112-113 — The Earth's Structure

Q1 a) 1.6 × 10 000 = 16 000 cm = 160 m or 0.16 km
b) 1.6 × 20 000 = 32 000 cm = 0.32 km
0.32 km + 325 km = 325.32 km

Q2 The main earthquake zones are along the plate boundaries.

Q3 A sphere showing 3 layers.
Labels: Crust (outer layer) — e.g. very thin, average 20 km thickness.
Mantle (next layer down) — e.g. properties of a solid but flows very slowly like a liquid. Radioactive decay takes place here.
Core (centre) — e.g. mostly iron and nickel.

Q4 Lithosphere — Made up of a 'jigsaw' of plates
Continental crust — A thin layer of rock forming most of the land
Convection current — Caused largely by radioactive decay within the Earth
Tectonic plates — Large pieces of crust and upper mantle
Eurasian Plate — Moving away from the North American Plate but toward the African Plate
Earthquakes — Caused by sudden movements of plates
Volcanoes — Hot spots that often sit on plate boundaries
San Andreas Fault — A well-known plate boundary in North America

Q5 a) Jo is wrong. Most of the heat in the centre of the Earth comes from radioactive decay.
b) i) the core
ii) iron and nickel (mostly)
iii) The inner core is solid, but the outer core is liquid.

Pages 114-115 — Evidence for Plate Tectonics

Q1 Pangaea, continents, plate tectonics, living creatures, fossils (the last two can be in either order)

Q2 a) The continents are too far apart for plants to spread this way. (NB birds probably hadn't evolved when Pangaea broke up.)
b) That the continents were once joined and have since separated.

Q3 a) A and C. They have identical rock sequences.
b) Matching animal and plant fossils found in the rocks.

Module C2 — Rocks and Metals

Q4 a) False
b) True
c) False
d) False
e) False
f) True
g) True

Q5 E.g. The coastlines of South America and South Africa seem to match.
Fossils of identical plants and animals were found on different continents.
Rocks with matching layers have been found on different continents.
Living creatures, such as a particular earthworm, are found on both sides of the Atlantic Ocean.

Pages 116-117 — Volcanic Eruptions

Q1 a) Magma is molten rock below the Earth's surface.
Lava is molten rock above the Earth's surface.
b) Igneous rock is formed by molten rock cooling and solidifying.
c) The composition of the molten rock and how quickly it cools.

Q2
1. Continental crust and oceanic crust collide.
2. The denser oceanic crust is forced underground (subduction).
3. Rock melts underground, forming magma.
4. Molten rock forces its way to the surface, forming a volcano.

Q3 a)

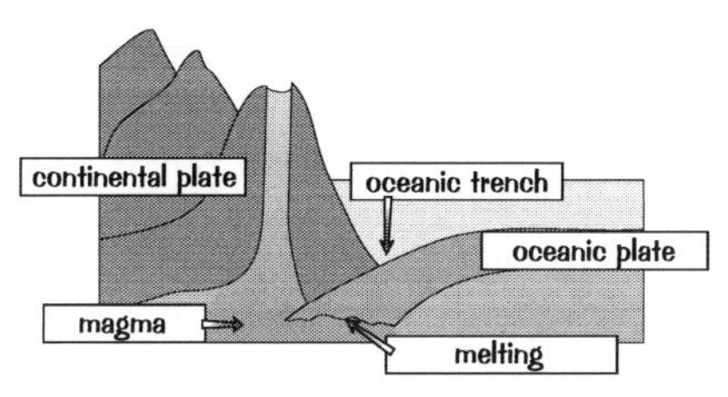

b) When one plate is forced under another / when an oceanic plate is forced under a continental plate.
c) It melts (and starts to rise).

Q4 a) The Nazca plate melts as it is forced under the South American plate. The magma finds its way up through the crust, causing volcanoes.
b) The plates grinding past each other causes earthquakes.
c) An oceanic trench forms where the oceanic plate is forced down under the continental plate.
d) Mountains are formed as the continental plate crumples.

Q5 a) The lava is runny and early warning is possible.
b) Explosive eruptions can hurl pumice, volcanic ash and bombs of lava with little warning.
c) The soil is very fertile. Some people have no choice (maybe they can't afford to live elsewhere).
d) Different sized pieces of pumice and ash are released. They form layers, usually with the bigger fragments on the bottom.

Pages 118-119 — The Evolution of the Atmosphere

Q1 True statements: When the Earth was formed, its surface was molten.
When some plants died and were buried under layers of sediment, the carbon they had removed from the atmosphere became locked up as fossil fuels.

Q2 The percentage of carbon dioxide has decreased by a large amount because it dissolved into the oceans and green plants used it for photosynthesis (and in both cases some of this carbon was incorporated into rocks, etc.).

Q3 The statements should be in this order (from the top of the timeline):
1. The atmosphere is about four-fifths nitrogen and one fifth oxygen.
2. More complex organisms evolved.
3. Oxygen built up due to photosynthesis, and the ozone layer developed.
4. Plant life appeared.
5. Water vapour condensed to form oceans.
6. The Earth cooled down slightly. A thin crust formed.
7. The Earth formed. There was lots of volcanic activity.

Q4 a) Largest sector is 'Nitrogen', second largest is 'Oxygen', smallest is 'Carbon dioxide and other gases'.
b) Nitrogen: 80% approx (to be more precise, it's 78% in dry air)
Oxygen: 20% approx (to be more precise, it's 21% in dry air)
Carbon dioxide: 0.035% approx
c) There is much more nitrogen and oxygen in today's atmosphere. There is far less carbon dioxide, water vapour and ammonia now. Oxygen is now a significant proportion of the atmosphere.
d) As the planet cooled, the water vapour condensed and formed the oceans.
e) Plants and microorganisms photosynthesised and produced it.
f) In any order:
Created the ozone layer which blocked harmful rays from the Sun.
Killed off early organisms/allowed more complex ones to evolve.
g) In any order:
Nitrogen was produced by ammonia reacting with oxygen.
Denitrifying bacteria released it.

Page 120 — The Carbon Cycle

Q1 a) burning
b) photosynthesis
c) respiration / burning
d) coal

Q2 A: decay/respiration; B: photosynthesis;
C: animal eating plant; D: you eating animal

Q3 E.g. More people means more respiration; more people need more land, which means less trees and less photosynthesis; more people need more energy, so more fossils fuels are burned.

Q4 E.g. three from: Only boiled the amount of water he needed/had a cold drink; eaten locally produced food; walked/cycled/used public transport instead of driving; used a more efficient car; worn warm clothes rather than turning on/up heating; gone on a holiday closer to home (using public transport); not left the TV and all the lights on (or used energy efficient bulbs on timers).

Page 121 — Air Pollution and Acid Rain

Q1 the greenhouse effect, sulfur dioxide, sulfuric, nitrogen oxides, nitric

Q2 a) It will react with acid rain and wear away.
b) Damage to plants; corrodes metal; acidifies lakes, killing fish.

Module C2 — Rocks and Metals

c) Using flue gas desulfurisation technology to remove sulfur dioxide from the gases released.

Q3 a) E.g. breathing difficulties, headaches and tiredness. Also contributes to smog.

b) oxygen, sunlight, oxides of nitrogen

Q4 a) There's not enough oxygen in engines so incomplete combustion occurs.

b) It prevents blood carrying oxygen around the body, which can lead to death.

Q5 a) i) carbon monoxide + nitrogen oxide → **nitrogen** + **carbon dioxide**

ii) $2CO + 2NO \rightarrow \mathbf{N_2} + \mathbf{2CO_2}$

b) Platinum and rhodium

Page 122 — Chemical Reaction Rates

Q1 Slow: an apple rotting; oil paint drying
Moderate speed: hair being dyed
Fast: a firework exploding; a match burning

Q2 a) True
b) False
c) True
d) True

Q3 a) A gas is produced and is lost from the reaction mixture.

b) By measuring the volume of gas produced at regular time intervals with a gas syringe.

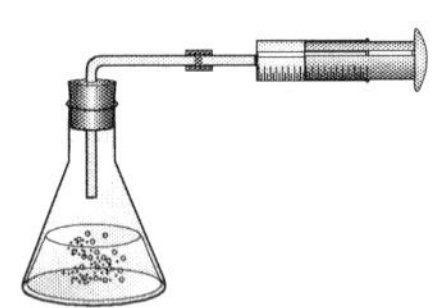

c) Nothing is lost from the reaction mixture so the mass would not change.

Q4 E.g. whether they collide and whether they collide with enough energy to react.

Pages 123-125 — Collision Theory

Q1 increasing the temperature — makes the particles move faster, so they collide more often
decreasing the concentration — means fewer particles of reactant are present, so fewer collisions occur
adding a catalyst — provides a surface for particles to stick to and lowers activation energy
increasing the surface area — means more of a solid reactant will be exposed to the other reactant

Q2 a) i) increase

ii) The particles are closer together so there are more collisions.

b)

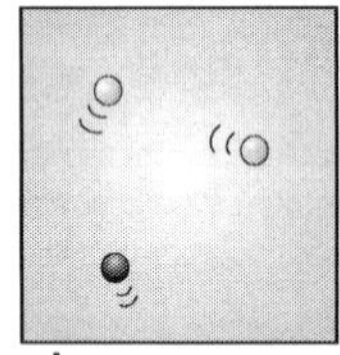

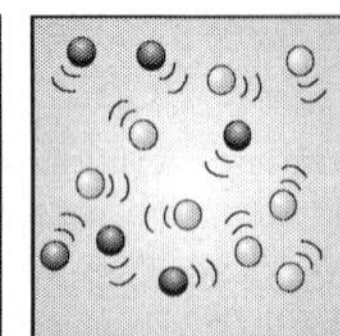

Q3 a) False
b) True
c) False
d) True
e) False

Q4 a) Catalysts often give the reacting particles a surface to stick to which makes it easier for them to react. They also reduce the energy needed by the particles before they react.

b) increase

Q5 faster, increases, energy, successful, speeding up

Q6 a) False
b) True
c) True
d) False
e) True

Q7 a) B

b) i) Curve C should be between curves A and B. It should level off at same height. See below.

ii) Curve D should level off at half the value that the other graphs do. See below.

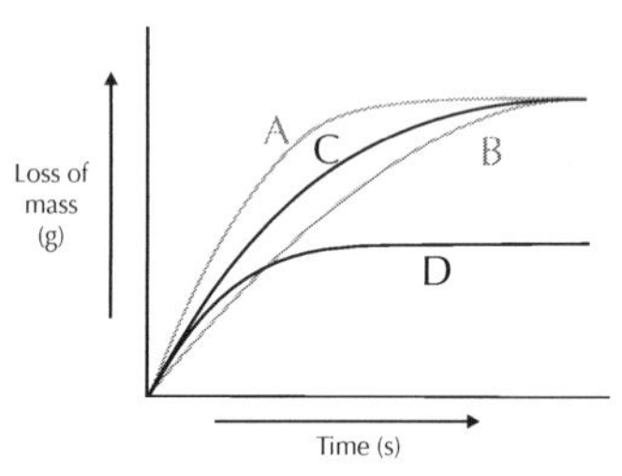

c) Size of marble pieces.

d) No, you cannot tell if it was a fair test. The same mass of marble chips was used each time but it is not known if the same volume of HCl was used each time or if, e.g., the temperature was kept constant.

Q8 a), b)

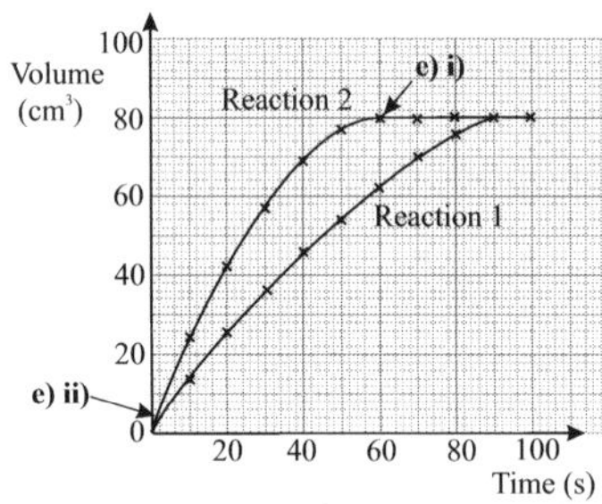

c) Reaction 2. Its graph is steeper and it levels off first.

d) E.g. 3 from: different temperature, different acid concentration, different sized marble chips, use of a catalyst.

e) i) see above

ii) see above

f) Draw tangents on each graph at 20 s and find their gradients. Reaction 1 is approximately 1.1 cm^3/s, Reaction 2 is approximately 1.6 cm^3/s.

g) Yes

h) about 30 cm^3

Q9 Fine powders have a very big surface area so they will burn very quickly when dispersed in the air. They can explode if there's a spark.

Pages 126-128 — Mixed Questions — Module C2

Q1 a) Layers of sediment are laid down in lakes or seas. The layers get buried under more layers and the water is squeezed out under pressure over millions of years. Minerals are deposited as fluids flow through the sediment.

b) $CaCO_3 \rightarrow CaO + CO_2$

Module P2 — Living for the Future

c)

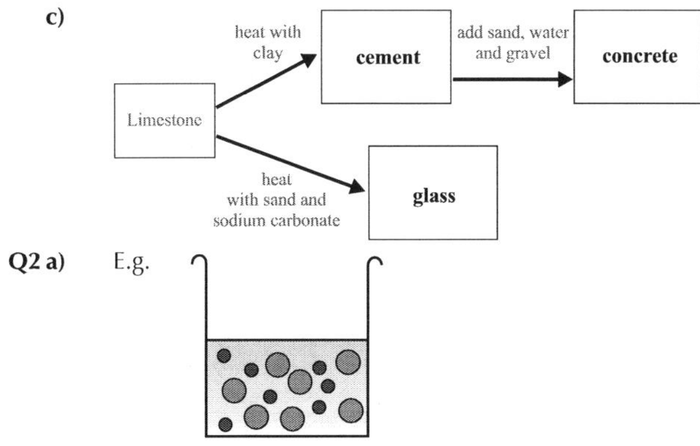

Q2 a) E.g.

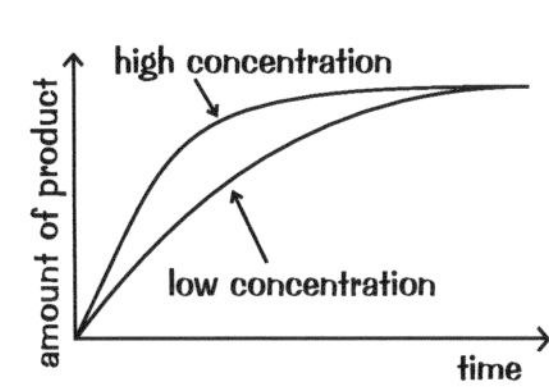

b) The reaction rate will increase because there are more reactant molecules in a given volume — this makes collisions between the reactants more likely.

c)

high concentration
low concentration
amount of product
time

d) E.g. any two of: volume/amount of acid, amounts of other reactants, temperature, presence or absence of catalyst.

Q3 a) Ores are minerals or rocks that it is worthwhile extracting metals from.

b) brass, bronze

c) The cathode is on the left. The anode is on the right.

d) The electrical supply pulls electrons off copper atoms at the anode, causing them to go into solution as Cu^{2+} ions.

e) the cathode

f) Wiring. It's an excellent electrical conductor.

g) E.g. aluminium, which is used for engine parts because it has a low density and is strong. / Iron, which is used for car body because it's strong and cheap.

h) Recycling metals takes less energy than extracting new ones does. This means less fossil fuels are burned and less carbon dioxide emitted.

Q4 a) The oceanic plate is forced under the continental plate.

b) i) The heat generated as one plate is forced under the other causes the rock to melt, forming magma.

ii) As the continental plate collides it crumples and forms mountains.

c) An oceanic trench.

Q5 a) E.g. granite, gabbro

b) E.g. basalt, rhyolite

c) melting

d) heat and pressure

Q6 a) Similarly to Earth's early atmosphere, there is a very high percentage of carbon dioxide and little oxygen and nitrogen.

b) Compared to the Earth's current atmosphere there is a lot higher percentage of carbon dioxide on Mars, and much less oxygen and nitrogen.

c) Human activity is increasing the amount of carbon dioxide. We're also releasing many polluting gases such as sulfur dioxide, nitrogen oxides and carbon monoxide.

Q7 a) E.g. Thermochromic or phosphorescent pigments could be used on the tickets. This would be harder for people to replicate (and they wouldn't necessarily even know that they had been used on the tickets).

b) The oil has to be oxidised by oxygen before it turns solid. With emulsion paint the water just has to evaporate.

Module P2 — Living for the Future

Page 129 — Using the Sun's Energy

Q1 silicon, semiconductor, atoms, electrons, electrons, DC

Q2 a) Direct current flows the same way round the circuit all the time.

b) The higher the sunlight intensity, the higher the power output.
The greater the surface area the greater the power output.

Q3 a) Any two from: No moving parts. No need for fuel. Solar power is renewable. Solar cells don't pollute the environment.

b) E.g. they only work well when it's sunny, they are expensive to install.

Q4 a) i) A matt black surface absorbs radiation (e.g. light) well.

ii) The glass box lets the light in but doesn't let it out again (and keeps cold air out).

b) This is done to keep the panel pointing directly at the Sun, so that it absorbs more light and is more effective at heating the water.

Page 130 — Producing and Distributing Electricity

Q1 power stations, National, Grid, generated, consumers, farms.

Q2 The Sun. (Warm air heated by the Sun rises and is replaced by cold air moving into its place — wind.)

Q3
1. A fossil fuel such as coal is burned to release heat.
2. Water is heated in the boiler and turned to steam.
3. Hot steam rushes through a turbine and makes it spin.
4. The spinning turbine makes the generator spin too.
5. Electricity is produced by the spinning generator.

Q4
Fossil: coal, oil, natural gas
Nuclear: uranium
Biomass: wood

Q5 a) The supply of wood won't run out. / More trees can always be grown to replace wood that is used.

b) E.g. The carbon dioxide released from burning wood was removed from the atmosphere very recently by the tree as it grew (by photosynthesis), so overall there is no change in CO_2 level. The CO_2 released from burning coal was removed from the atmosphere millions of years ago, so burning coal increases the amount of carbon dioxide in the atmosphere today.

Pages 131-132 — The Dynamo Effect

Q1 a) Move the (vertical) wire repeatedly in and out of the magnetic field at an angle to the direction of the field (i.e. not parallel to the magnetic field).

b) The ammeter needle would move first in one direction, then back to zero and then in the opposite direction and back to zero again. It would continue like this as long as the wire was moving in and out of the magnetic field.

c) i) The ammeter would still move from one side to the other, but would start from the opposite side.

ii) The effect would be the same as in i) above.

Q2 a) It reverses direction.

b) a current / potential difference (voltage)

c) AC

Q3 The bicycle's wheels turn more slowly. This turns the dynamo more slowly and so a smaller voltage is produced. This reduces the current in the bulb and the light becomes dimmer.

Module P2 — Living for the Future

Q4 a) By pulling the magnet out again OR by turning the magnet round and pushing it into the coil OR by pushing the magnet into the coil from the left-hand side OR by turning the magnet around and pulling it out of the left-hand side of the coil.

b) By pushing the magnet in and immediately pulling it out again.

c) By rapidly pushing the magnet in and out of the coil a number of times.

d) Kinetic energy from the moving magnet is transferred via its magnetic field into electrical energy in the wire, which is then carried to the oscilloscope.

Q5 A

Page 133 — Supplying Electricity Efficiently

Q1
1. Electrical energy is generated in power stations.
2. The voltage of the supply is raised.
3. An electrical current flows through power cables across the country.
4. The voltage of the supply is reduced.
5. Mrs Miggins boils the kettle for tea.

Q2 a) The National Grid transmits energy at high voltage and low current.

b) A step-up transformer is used to raise the voltage of the supply before electricity is transmitted.

c) Using a low current makes sure there is not much energy wasted.

Q3

Total Energy Input (J)	Useful Energy Output (J)	Efficiency
2000	1500	**0.75 / 75%**
4000	2000	0.50
4000	**1000**	0.25

Q4 a) AC

b) With AC current, transformers can be used to change the voltage — transformers only work with AC.

Q5 Total energy input per second = 40 × 6 = 240 MJ/s.
Efficiency = 30% so total output = 240 × 30/100 = 72 MJ/s.
Total energy loss = 240 – 72 = **168 MJ/s** or **168 MW**.

Pages 134-135 — Power

Q1

Appliance	Power (W)	Current (A)
Kettle	2600	11.3
Radio	13	0.057
Laptop computer	736	3.2
Lamp	39.1	0.17

Q2 a) Units of energy = power × time = 2 kW × 3 h = **6 kWh**.

b) Cost = 6 kWh × 7p/kWh = **42p**.

c) Lamp: Energy used = 0.06 kW × 9 h = 0.54 kWh.
Shower: Energy used = 8 kW × 0.25 h = 2 kWh.
So Boris is **right** — the shower uses more energy.

Q3 a) 34783 – 34259 = **524 Units**.

b) Total cost = 524 × 9.7 = **5082.8p** (or **£50.83** to the nearest penny).

Q4 a) Night storage heating. (Also accept e.g. washing machine or dishwasher run on a timer switch.)

b) i) It's cheaper.

ii) It's cost-effective because power stations can't be switched off at night, so it's better for power companies to sell electricity generated at night than to waste it.

Q5 a) Number of kWh used = 7 × 275 × 1000 = 1 925 000 kWh so cost = kWh × night time cost per kWh = 1 925 000 × 3.7 = 7 122 500p or **£71 225**.

b) kWh generated = 5 × 288 × 1000 = 1 440 000 kWh so cost = kWh × daytime cost per kWh = 1 440 000 × 7.2 = 10 368 000 or **£103 680**.

Q6 a) 230 × 10 = 2300 = 2.30 kW.

b) Units used = 2.30 × 2 = 4.6.
Cost on peak = 4.6 × 11.3 = 51.98p.
Cost off peak = 4.6 × 6.0 = 27.60p
Saving = 51.98 – 27.60 = **24.38p**
Or 4.6 × (11.3 – 6.0) = **24.38p**

Page 136 — Power Sources for the Future

Q1 a) Any two from: they spoil the view/natural environment, they are noisy, birds are killed when they fly into them.

b) Any two from: it is a renewable source of energy, once the turbines are installed it doesn't cause pollution/greenhouse gas emissions, no fuel is needed to operate the turbines, wind turbines leave no permanent scarring of the landscape when they are removed.

Q2 a) A nuclear reactor uses **uranium** to make heat.

b) Nuclear power stations are **more expensive** to build than coal-fired power stations and they **take longer** to start up.

Q3 Any three from: Nuclear power stations are expensive to build. There is a risk of catastrophic accidents. Nuclear power stations may be a target for terrorists. It produces radioactive waste which is dangerous and hard to get rid of (or reprocess). Processing spent nuclear fuel causes pollution. Old worn out nuclear power stations have to be decommissioned and this is expensive.

Q4 a) E.g. nuclear power doesn't produce greenhouse gases so it doesn't contribute to global warming, nuclear fuels (uranium) are likely to be readily available for longer than fossil fuels.

b) E.g. it is a more reliable source of energy / it is not dependent on the weather like some renewables.

Q5 fuel rods, uranium, plutonium, uranium, plutonium, nuclear weapons.

Pages 137-138 — Nuclear Radiation

Q1 electrons, ions, less far, more.

Q2

Radiation Type	Ionising power weak/moderate/strong	Charge positive/-none/negative	Relative mass no mass/small/large	Penetrating power low/moderate/high	Relative speed slow/fast/very fast
alpha	strong	positive	large	low	slow
beta	moderate	negative	small	moderate	fast
gamma	weak	none	no mass	high	very fast

Q3 a) i) T

ii) T

iii) T

iv) F

b) iv) Beta particles are electrons but they do come from the nucleus (when a neutron turns into a proton and an electron).

Module P2 — Living for the Future

Q4 Alpha particles are the biggest and slowest of the three types of radiation, so are most likely to collide with the atoms of a material and ionise them. Gamma rays have no mass and move much faster than alpha particles, so they are much less likely to collide with an atom and ionise it.

Q5 a) A: gamma. B: alpha. C: beta.

b) Gamma rays have no charge — they are just energy — so they are not attracted or repelled by an electric field.

c) A magnetic field.

d) i) The counters were recording natural background radiation.

ii) Measure the count rate (counts per minute) from natural background radiation and subtract this figure from the readings recorded when the sources were present.

Pages 139-140 — Uses of Nuclear Radiation

Q1
1. The radioactive source emits alpha particles.
2. The air between the electrodes is ionised by the alpha particles.
3. A current flows between the electrodes — the alarm stays off.
4. A fire starts and smoke particles absorb the alpha radiation.
5. The circuit is broken so no current flows.
6. The alarm sounds.

Q2 Beta radiation is used because it can pass through paper, but the amount of radiation which passes through will depend on the thickness of the paper. (Alpha would not pass through at all and gamma would always pass through.)

Q3 a) A gamma-emitter with a long half-life is used. Gamma radiation is needed because it is not stopped by air or metal parts of the instruments and can kill the cells of living organisms (e.g. bacteria) on the instruments. A long half-life is needed because the sterilising machine will be in use over many years and replacing the source frequently would be inconvenient.

b) Lead is used to prevent the operator and anyone near the machine from getting too high a dose of radiation.

c) It kills or damages any living cells in the fruit — including the ones in insects and in microbes which make the fruit decay.

Q4 Gamma radiation would pass easily through any cracked areas in the turbine blade but would be absorbed to a greater extent by the un-cracked areas. So cracks would show up as high gamma energy at the detector.

Q5 a) Alpha radiation would not penetrate the pipe or the surface layer of soil and could not be detected on the surface. The long half-life means that it remains potentially dangerous for a longer time.
(They should use a **gamma**-emitter with a **short** half-life.)

b) They plan to inject the radioisotope at the wrong point.
It will flow away from the section of pipe being tested. They should inject the source at B.

Q6 a) The level of radioactivity from kidney A decreases faster than that from kidney B. This shows that kidney A is working much better and has passed the radioactive material on to the bladder.

b) An alpha source would do a lot of damage to the cells of the patient's kidneys, because alpha radiation is highly ionising. Also, the radiation could not be detected outside the body.

Pages 141-142 — Dangers from Radioactive Materials

Q1 a) E.g. He isn't wearing protective gloves. He isn't using tongs to hold the sample. He is pointing the sample directly in the face of the other scientist.

b) By having the samples out for the minimum time.

c) In a thick-walled lead-lined container.

Q2 a) E.g. By using remote-controlled machinery e.g. a robot arm. The radioactive material could be put in a lead-lined box. The workers could wear lead-lined suits.

b) E.g. By using lead screens, and ensuring that buildings are protected by thick walls made of concrete or lead.

Q3 B: Protective suit. Protects against dust, alpha, beta and some gamma radiation.
C: Lead shield. Protects against full range of radiation.
D: Robot arm. Keeps worker as far from radioactive source as possible.

Q4 a) E.g. used clothing, paper, gloves, syringes (that have been contaminated with radioactive material).

b) It's buried in secure landfill sites.

Q5 a) tens of thousands of years

b) It is sealed into glass blocks. The blocks are then sealed into metal canisters

c) The site must not be prone to earthquakes because earthquakes could break canisters of radioactive material and let the material leak out. Radioactive material could get into ground water.

Pages 143-144 — Earth's Magnetic Field

Q1 a) b) c)

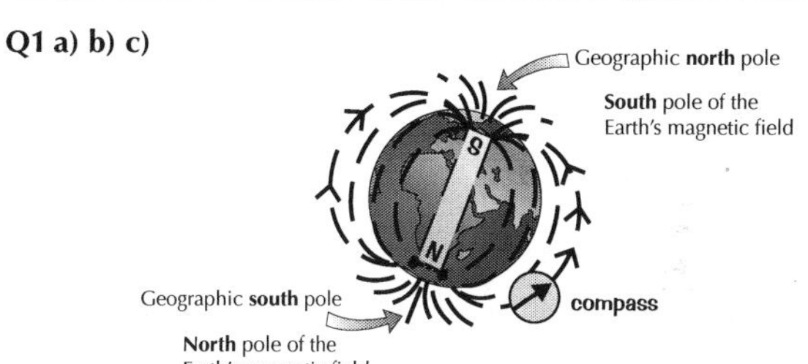

Q2 a) molten iron

b) Pass an electric current through the coil of wire.

c) Outside the coil, the field is similar to that of a bar magnet. Inside the coil the field lines are straight.
E.g.

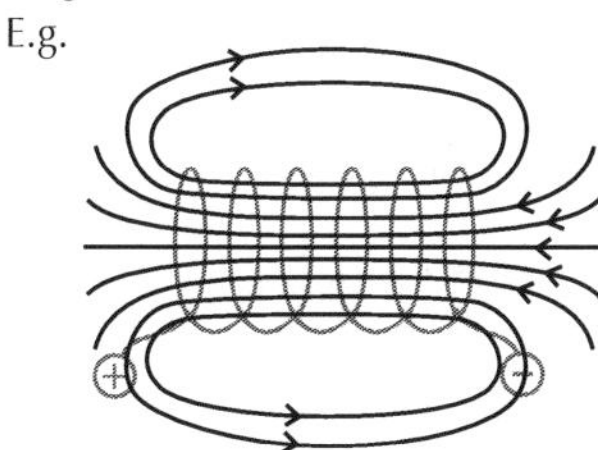

Q3 Suspend the magnet on the string so that it can turn freely in a level plane. The N pole of the magnet should point to the geographic North Pole of the Earth. Jack should follow this direction because Ghana lies to the North.

Q4 When the switch is closed a current flows in the coil. This produces a magnetic field through the coil. This magnetic field repels the magnetised iron bolt, making it move to the right. This releases the bolt from the lock and allows the door to open.

Q5 a) The Moon is less dense than the Earth: The Moon could be made from the low density bits that flew off from the collision.

Module P2 — Living for the Future

b) The Moon doesn't have a big iron core, but the Earth does: The iron core of the colliding planet merged with the Earth's — none of it formed a core on the Moon.

c) The Moon is made of materials with high melting points and boiling points: All the low boiling point materials would have boiled away in the high temperatures following the collision.

Page 145 — Particles and Rays from the Sun

Q1 a) One of: they ionise the gases in the atmosphere, they create gamma rays.

b) i) They are strongly ionising could damage or destroy cells in the organisms.

ii) It deflects them. It also traps some of them inside the magnetic field.

Q2 Massive clouds of charged particles which can reach the Earth and produce disturbances in the Earth's magnetic field.

Q3 a) Three from: telecommunications, navigation/GPS, weather forecasting, spying. (Or other sensible answers.)

b) The charged particles emitted in the solar flare can cause power surges in electrical wiring (due to electromagnetic induction).

Q4 a) Polar lights are 'curtains of light' in the sky visible from near the poles.

b) Charged particles fall through the atmosphere. Some of their energy is transferred to particles in the atmosphere — causing them to emit light.

Pages 146-147 — The Solar System

Q1

Body	Mars	Jupiter	Asteroids	Venus	Saturn	Neptune	Earth	Mercury	Uranus
Number	4	6	5	2	7	9	3	1	8

Q2 1) The planets do not give out their own light *OR* the planets only reflect light.
2) The planets are much smaller than the stars.
3) The planets are much closer than the stars.

Q3 a) Venus does not emit its own light.

b)

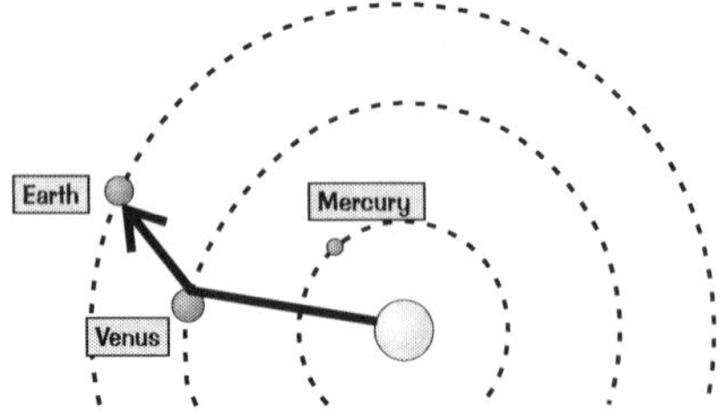

Q4 a) i) Towards the centre of the circle.

ii) a centripetal force

b) gravity

c)

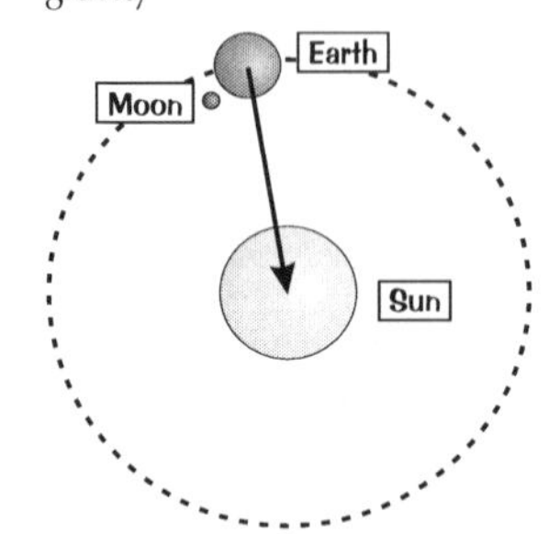

d) The force of gravity decreases very rapidly with distance (force is inversely proportional to distance^2). The Sun is much further from the Moon than the Earth, so its gravitational pull is not strong enough to overcome the pull of the Earth's gravity (despite the Sun's greater mass).

Q5

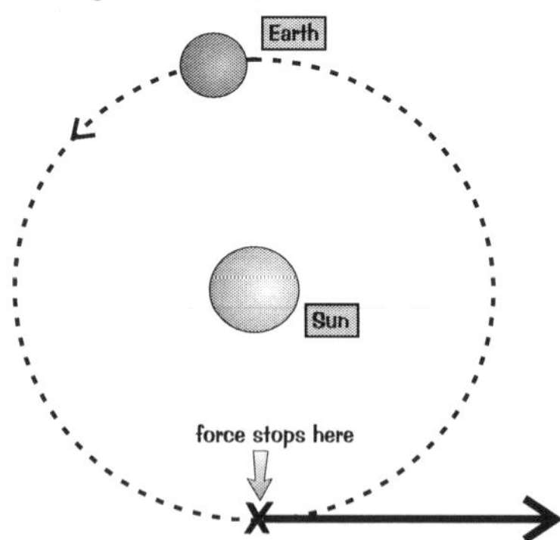

Pages 148-149 — Asteroids and Comets

Q1 a) Mars, Jupiter (either way round).

b) D

Q2 Meteors, atmosphere, burn up, shooting stars, meteors, meteorites

Q3 a) There are big craters, layers of unusual elements in rocks that must have come from an asteroid, and sudden changes in the numbers of fossils between one layer of rock and the next.

b) E.g. When the asteroid hit Earth the impact created a big dust cloud which spread around the Earth and blocked out sunlight over a very large area for months/years. As a result, the global temperature fell/ the climate changed, killing off many green plants and the food chains that depended on them.

Q4 a) Asteroids and comets that might be on a collision course with Earth.

b) To find out if they will strike the Earth and, if they will, to plan action to deal with them.

Q5 a) an ellipse / elliptical

b) i) C

ii) A

c) The Sun's gravity exerts a force on the comet accelerating it towards the Sun. It picks up speed as it moves towards the Sun.

d) i) Rock, dust and ice.

ii) The ice in the comet melts as it approaches the Sun and gets hotter.

Q6 E.g. The planets, especially Jupiter (the largest planet), all exert a gravitational pull on the asteroids. This pull is strong enough to overcome the gravitational attraction of one asteroid for another, so it prevents them clumping together.

Page 150 — Beyond the Solar System

Q1 C

Q2 a) It is the distance travelled in one year by light travelling in a vacuum.

b) $(3 \times 10^8) \times 24 \times 60 \times 60 \times 365.25 \div 1000$
$= \mathbf{9.47 \times 10^{12}}$ **km** (to 3 significant figures).

c) Assuming that we are approximately 25 000 light years from the centre of the galaxy, then
$25\,000 \times 9.467 \times 10^{12} = 2.5 \times 10^4 \times 9.467 \times 10^{12}$
$= 23.668 \times 10^{16}$ km $= \mathbf{2.37 \times 10^{17}}$ **km** (to 3 s.f.).

Module P2 — Living for the Future

Q3 a) Black holes are made of very dense material. They have extremely strong gravitational fields which attract everything, even light. Because light cannot escape from the region of the black hole, the black hole appears black.

b) E.g. Scientists can observe X-rays emitted by hot gases from other stars as they spiral into the black hole.

Page 151 — Exploring the Solar System

Q1 Any four of: Need to supply sufficient food, water, and oxygen. Need for temperature control, waste management. Need to alleviate stress, muscle wastage and boredom. Need for sufficient fuel to lift off and carry all of the above.

Q2 a) Any two from: They're cheaper than manned probes. They can penetrate dangerous radiation zones. There's no need to carry food, etc. There's more payload available for instruments. They can accelerate faster without risk of the G force harming crew. There's no risk of astronauts losing their lives if the craft crashes.

b) E.g. they cannot think for themselves, they cannot self-repair so well.

Q3 a) Data on temperature, magnetism, gravity and radiation, atmospheric composition etc. can all be collected without landing.

b) i) Some/all of the above, plus information about the planet's surface — it could collect and analyse samples of dust, rocks etc., take photographs, search for particular features.

ii) E.g. If the probe deviates even slightly from its planned descent it may not slow down enough, so it may be damaged by overheating during descent, or by crash-landing.
Or it may land on an unsuitable (e.g. very rocky) part of the surface, also causing damage on impact.

Page 152 — The Origin of the Universe

Q1 a) matter, energy, explosion, expand, age, expansion.

b) Because we do not know how much the rate of expansion has changed since the Big Bang.

Q2 It will sound lower pitched.

Q3 As the train leaves, it moves away from Brian's microphone. So the frequency appears to get slightly **lower**. E.g.

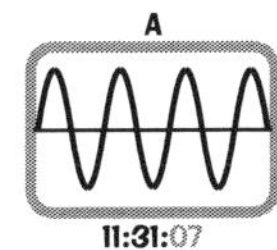

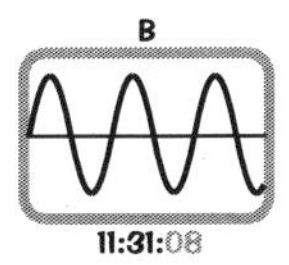

Q4 E.g. Light from other galaxies is red-shifted — all the frequencies are lower in the spectrum than is the case for other objects nearby. This tells us that the galaxies are moving away from us. Also, the further away the galaxy, the greater the red-shift so more distant galaxies must be moving away faster than nearer ones i.e. the whole Universe must be expanding. The low frequency radiation coming from all parts of the Universe — cosmic background radiation — tells us that the Universe has been expanding and cooling.

Page 153 —The Life Cycle of Stars

Q1 a) Heat (from thermonuclear fusion)

b) Gravity

c) The force pulling the star inwards and the force pushing it outwards are equal, so they balance and cancel out.

d) A main sequence star

Q2 a) Gravitational attraction pulls the material together.

b) Energy is released when hydrogen nuclei fuse together to form helium nuclei / from thermonuclear fusion.

Q3 a) It runs out of hydrogen.

b) Its surface is cooler than a main sequence star's surface.

Q4 planetary nebula, white dwarf, supernova, neutron star, black hole.

Q5 E.g. It glows brightly again as it undergoes more fusion reactions and forms heavier elements. It expands and contracts several times before eventually exploding in a supernova.

Pages 154-156 — Mixed Questions — Module P2

Q1 a) i) The heat is used to turn water into steam, which drives turbines. Generators then convert the kinetic energy of the turbine blades into electrical energy.

ii) Find the total energy input and subtract the 1000 J of useful output.
Fuel Energy Input = Electrical Energy Output ÷ Efficiency
= 1000 J ÷ 0.38 = 2632 J.
So wasted energy = 2632 – 1000 = **1632 J**.

iii) The Sun. The Sun's energy was converted into chemical energy by green plants (photosynthesis). Some of the plants were consumed by animals. The plants and animals died and were buried, eventually becoming fossil fuels, e.g. gas, which contain that chemical energy.

b) i) nuclear energy, biomass

ii) Both solar and wind power are unreliable / dependent on the weather. / On days which weren't sunny or windy, there would be little or no electricity.

c) i) So that the current required to transmit power can be low, which reduces the energy wasted through heating in the cables.

ii) The high voltage is 'stepped down' using a series of transformers before it reaches people's homes or businesses.

Q2 a)

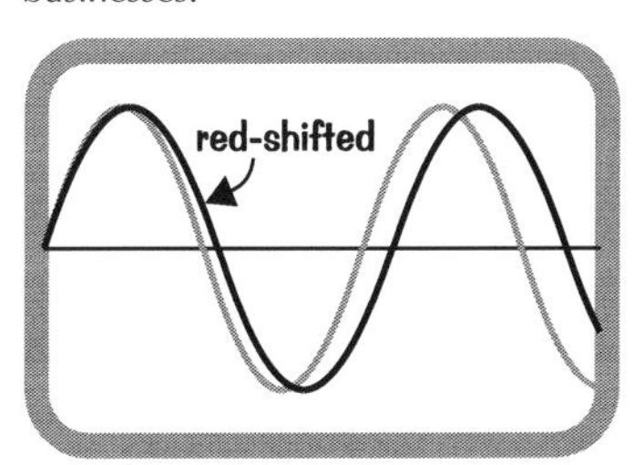

b) More distant galaxies have greater red-shifts than nearer ones, showing that more distant galaxies are moving away from us faster. This is evidence that the Universe is expanding and started in a very dense (and hot) state.

Q3 a) P = VI so, rearranging, I = 360 ÷ 230 = **1.57 A**.

b) Energy = Power × Time = 0.36 kW × 0.75 h = 0.27 kWh.
Cost = 0.27 × 15.2 = **4p**.

Q4 a) i) Americium-241. Alpha radiation is strongly ionising but is absorbed by smoke particles. The radiation is absorbed by a few centimetres of air, so it won't be hazardous. Americium-241 decays very slowly, so it won't need replacing for many years.

Module P2 — Living for the Future

ii) Technetium-99m. It emits gamma radiation, which can pass out of the body, and it decays very quickly, so it causes as little damage as possible to the patient.

b) It's a source of beta and gamma radiation so workers should be protected by full protective (lead-lined) suits and/or screens/barriers made from thick lead or concrete.

Q5 a) An AC voltage is induced in the coil because the coil experiences a magnetic field which is varying in direction and strength. An alternating current flows in the wire and the lamp lights up.

b) i) You wouldn't notice any difference. (The induced voltage would be in the opposite direction when the magnet is at any given position, but the size of the AC voltage and current would not change.)

ii) The lamp would be brighter.

Q6 a) Hydrogen nuclei combine (by thermonuclear fusion) to form helium nuclei. Over time more and more of the hydrogen is used up, producing more and more helium.

b) The size of the star. / The amount of hydrogen contained in the star.

c) No — this only happens to very massive stars and the Sun is not massive enough.

Q7 The molten iron core causes the Earth to have a magnetic field and the 'northern lights' occur because the Earth's magnetic field deflects charged particles towards the poles. Without a molten core to set up the magnetic field, this deflection would not occur.

Q8 a) Asteroids are rocks / piles of rock, from 1km to 1000 km across, which orbit the Sun. When asteroids collide with the Earth, they can cause widespread destruction, climate change and mass extinctions.

b) Because the pull of the Sun's gravity is greater. (The force of gravity between two objects is stronger the closer the objects are.)

Q9 a) Neptune

b) E.g. The spacecraft would have to take a lot of fuel, so it would be heavy and expensive. It would probably take years to reach the planet, and carrying enough food, water and oxygen to keep the astronauts alive would be very expensive. Protecting the astronauts from long-term exposure to cosmic rays, psychological stress, and the effects of low gravity on their muscles and bones would be very difficult.

ISBN 978 1 84146 715 3
9 781841 467153

SRHA41